Buse[s]

Restored 2002

Buses
Restored 2002

Compiled in association with
the National Association of
Road Transport Museums

First published 2002

ISBN 0 7110 2900 8

© Ian Allan Publishing Ltd 2002

Published by Ian Allan Publishing

an imprint of Ian Allan Publishing Ltd, Hersham, Surrey
KT12 4RG.
Printed by Ian Allan Printing Ltd, Hersham, Surrey
KT12 4RG.

Code: 0204/B

Note: Please be aware that vehicles on display
can vary from time to time as not all museums
display their entire 'fleet'. Visitors wishing to see a
particular vehicle should make enquiries prior to
their visit.

Front cover: **New to Bristol Tramways in 1955 this
Bristol KSW6B is preserved at the West Midlands
Bus Preservation Society's site.** *Philip Lamb*

Back cover: **Chesterfield Corporation's Daimler
Fleetline CRL6-30 is in the care of the Chesterfield
123 Group.** *Philip Lamb*

Half title: **Memory Lane Vintage Omnibus Services
operate these two former Royal Blue ECW-bodied
Bristol MW6Gs.** *Philip Lamb*

Title page: **HPW 133 is a 1949 Bristol K5G/ECW
which was initially loaned to London Transport
before being operated by Eastern National
Omnibus Co.** *Steve Milner*

Contents

Useful addresses

NARTM, PO Box 5141, Burton-upon-Trent DE15 OZF.

The Transport Trust, 202 Lambeth Road, London
SE1 7JW.

British Bus Preservation Group, 18 Greenriggs,
Hedley Park, Stopsley, Luton LU2 9TQ.

The PSV Circle, 26 Ashville Grove, Halifax HX2 OPN.

Introduction and Background

Welcome to the third annual edition of *Buses Restored*. The first edition, published in 2000, listed well over 1200 buses and coaches in preservation in the British Isles. As a result, many other groups have contacted Ian Allan and NARTM and have asked to have their own collections included in the database while some groups have moved from Part 2 to Part 1 as their ambitions to allow the public to view their vehicles have come to fruition.

In addition to those vehicles listed here, the NARTM database contains details of many more buses and coaches whose owners do not wish to have their details published at present. Some of these are in private ownership and their owners do not want potential visitors to their storage locations, which range from agricultural barns through industrial yards to parking at the side of the house – with the consent of a tolerant family and neighbours! It is unfortunate that a small minority of enthusiasts have a tendency to 'acquire' rare items, such as badges and destination blinds, so we must respect the privacy and wishes of these vehicle owners. We hope that the security and integrity of the NARTM database will encourage yet more owners to allow us to add their vehicles to the list, in order that we can continue to build the best possible view of the range of historic buses and coaches still in existence.

The NARTM database can be used in several ways. An obvious benefit is to put owners in touch with others who own similar vehicles so that spare parts may be shared or sourced. In some instances bulk purchases of new materials have been arranged by owners and collections who look after similar buses and this can reduce restoration costs significantly. It is also important to know how many historic buses and coaches are still in existence in order that organisations such as NARTM can work with the Transport Trust and the needs of our sector of transport preservation can be seen alongside the needs of others. Steam engines, of both the rail and road varieties, must have expensive boiler inspections every few years, historic aircraft have airframes that need specialist maintenance while boats must be maintained in a watertight condition if they are not to sink. All these areas of transport preservation have to compete with each other and many others for the limited resources that may be available to them.

What does a bus need to survive for future generations to admire and observe? Many current bus companies park their vehicles outside when they are not in use, so why can older vehicles not exist in similar conditions? In Britain's damp climate, changes in temperature open up seams between body panels, allowing rainwater to trickle inside the bodywork. Over time this will cause the timber frames of older buses to rot and steel frames will rust away. This process happens much more quickly with vehicles that are left to stand outside for a length of time, while service buses regularly warm up and move through the air, which can slow the process of corrosion. Therefore, what old buses and coaches need more than anything is a roof over their own roofs. A building with walls adds further protection from the weather (and also from small boys with stones, to whom bus windows are sadly a great attraction). A secure building, ideally with temperature and humidity controls is what such vehicles really need if they are to remain in good condition to educate and amaze future generations.

Some collections in this book have been given a major boost in the provision of secure storage and display buildings in recent years by the award of grant funding from the Heritage Lottery Fund (HLF) and other organisations. Such awards are the result of many months and years of hard work behind the scenes, filling in application forms, drawing up business plans and cash flow projections – all of which are far removed from the activities of vehicle restoration and driving which many enthusiasts imagined lay ahead when they became involved with the hobby. To other groups, running a museum is their primary objective and a small number of the collections described in this book are operated by professional people. The support given by the HLF and other bodies to amateur museum keepers and vehicle preservationists is very gratefully received and we are pleased to acknowledge their assistance here.

Other vehicles are owned by people and groups who have consciously decided not to display their collections to the public except at rallies and at other events. A large number of buses and coaches are owned in this way and many have been authentically restored to their original glory, which is a tribute to those working in often difficult conditions with resources of time and money, which are frequently very limited. While many of these vehicles are kept in secure, dry conditions at present, the future for some may not be so rosy. Indeed, the future for a number of vehicles that form part of collections open to the public may not be as secure in the long term as it may appear at first glance. Their owners may become too old to look after them properly and in some cases they may once again be left to rot or to be scrapped. At the end of the day there is only a finite amount of resources available to secure the long-term survival of historic buses and coaches and it is sadly almost inevitable that some of those listed here will suffer this fate. A number of buses, which were once well known on the rally fields and show grounds of Britain in the 1960s and 1970s have already been lost.

However, by being included in *Buses Restored 2002* and being part of the NARTM database, buses and coaches are at least known to a wider audience and by updating the database each year a check can be kept on those which might be in danger of falling by the wayside. A further use of the database then, could be as part of a process to determine which are the really important examples; those which must be saved – almost as 'National Treasures' in some cases. There will be relatively few in this category – the Imperial War Museum's First World War veteran London B Type bus known as "'Ole Bill" might be a prime candidate. If other important vehicles were felt to be at risk, and there were no similar vehicles listed on the database, then the case for seeking and providing some funding to secure their long term future could be strengthened, while they may not be so significant if other similar examples still exist.

Just what makes a vehicle 'important' can be a very subjective thing – it may be important to some because they travelled to school on it, to others it represents a technical milestone and to yet more people it may be almost an icon – like the familiar red London Routemasters which have been a part of the scene in the capital for almost half a century. In other parts of the country, quite different buses were part of the local scene for long periods of time and are equally important in their own way.

NARTM has decided to face this challenge head on and to try and devise a set of objective questions, which could help to establish which vehicles really deserve to have a long-term future. There is absolutely no intention to score each vehicle in existence, or to set one vehicle against another. However, the time may come when someone (not NARTM) has to decide which buses should be saved and which ones have to take their chance in a commercial world, which may all too often lead to their demise. Such vehicles may also be lost to preservation through export and conversion to caravans, burger bars and the like. A fair means of assessing the historic merit of a particular vehicle may well help ensure its survival in the future.

As vehicle preservation only really started in the late 1950s, only a small proportion of the historic buses in existence today date from before the end of the Second World War. Early buses from the 1920s and before were developing rapidly and had relatively short lives. Their timber-framed bodies did not last long as the solid tyres jolted along the cobbled streets and quickly rotted away in Britain's damp climate. Even the technically advanced buses and coaches of the 1930's saw years of hard work during the war and only a few survived to be preserved, with a number of examples tantalisingly being scrapped just as the preservation movement was gaining momentum. Those surviving examples from the earlier years of the development of buses and coaches are now especially important in illustrating the evolution of motorised public road transport.

NARTM would welcome readers' thoughts on this subject and you can contact us through the PO Box number shown at the end of the Introduction.

At some point, however, an objective view will need to be taken to establish which vehicles are worthy of an assured future, possibly even a future supported by public funding. Unfortunately it is unlikely that all those buses and coaches in existence today will survive in the long term, although who would have predicted 35 years ago just how many steam railway engines would still be in working order in the twenty first century? It is hoped that NARTM and its member organisations can play their part in raising the profile of historic buses and coaches and also work towards providing that long-term future for as many vehicles as reasonably possible. In the mean time, please enjoy browsing through this book and we hope that you will be encouraged to visit many of the collections described in its pages.

What is NARTM ?

The National Association of Road Transport Museums (NARTM) is an informal organisation of museums and collections. Volunteers operate many of them, although others, such as the Glasgow and London Transport Museums, are managed by full-time staff. This mix of museum types gives the opportunity to share ideas and experiences and the volunteers involved each bring their own professional skills to their projects and best practices can then be shared by all the member collections.

NARTM has been in existence for almost 20 years and now has around 40 member organisations, with more joining each year. The buses and coaches that form part of the NARTM collections are generally regarded as forming the nucleus of the National Collection of Buses and Coaches. However, it must be stressed that many important examples are in private hands outside the scope of NARTM and its members.

What does NARTM do?

Many of the people involved in running transport museums are busy people and have little spare time after making significant contributions to their own projects, such as the Museum in Manchester. This is why NARTM only holds two meetings each year at the various member museums and in recent years we have visited Devon, Lincoln, Glasgow, Oxford and Portsmouth. In between meetings, the quarterly *Bulletin* keeps members in touch with each other and we are often in touch. Indeed, one of the main functions of NARTM is to put people in touch with each other and there are many instances of restoration projects progressing and spare parts being located through NARTM contacts. Discussion topics at recent meetings have included the encouragement and role of Junior members, bus services, grant applications, museum registration, visitor facilities, risk assessment, documentation and links with other bodies.

NARTM's unique service to its members is also as an information exchange about running museums — after all, as so many of our members are volunteers, their skills and experiences are not within the heritage and leisure industry. It is often the case that another project in another area has already been faced with exactly the same issues as we have today, and by sharing ideas and pooling resources, progress can be made more quickly.

Over the years NARTM has also taken a lead role in campaigning on new legislation to lessen its impact on the historic bus preservation movement. Vehicle licensing, driver licensing, tachographs and the retention of original registration numbers have all received our attention, with some success in each case through our work in conjunction with other groups within the movement. NARTM is also a club authorised to endorse applications from historic vehicle owners to retain, or regain, the original registration of their vehicle.

The future

NARTM is currently working closely with the Transport Trust to define the bus preservation sector of the heritage transport industry. It is also addressing the major issues currently facing the movement — storage, documentation, human resources and skills, public access and the future of vehicles in preservation. A database is now maintained which lists all vehicles in NARTM and associated collections and this will eventually form part of a decision-making process to ensure that the most historically important vehicles have a secure long-term future.

For more information about NARTM please contact NARTM, PO Box 5141, Burton-upon-Trent, Staffordshire, DE15 0ZF.
Website: www.nartm.org.uk
e-mail: nartm@btinternet.com

Useful addresses

The Transport Trust, 202 Lambeth Road, London SE1 7JW.

British Bus Preservation Group, 18 Greenriggs, Hedley Park, Stopsley, Luton LU2 9TQ.

The PSV Circle, 26 Ashville Grove, Halifax HX2 0PN.

Midland Red C1 No 3301 (KHA 301) is currently part of the West Midlands Bus Preservation Society collection. *Philip Lamb*

How to Use this Book

This book lists both formal museums and the more informal types of collection, and gives details of opening times, contact addresses and the facilities available, together with a list of the buses, trolleybuses and coaches on display. Many of the sites are open to the public on a regular basis. Admission fees vary and some are even free to visitors, although donations towards the upkeep of the collections are always welcome. Please be aware that the vehicles on display can vary from time to time. Not all museums are able to display their entire 'fleet', and some practice the regular rotation of exhibits for added interest. In addition, some of the vehicles may be in the process of restoration in a workshop off-site, and there is always the possibility that a bus may be on loan to another museum! Visitors wishing to see a particular vehicle should make enquiries prior to the visit.

Some collections are not normally available for public access. However, the owners usually welcome visitors and will arrange for viewing by prior application. In addition, many such groups do have open or public days from time to time. Contact addresses are provided in this book, and those wishing to visit a particular site are asked to contact the address given. Please bear in mind that most are run by volunteers — please enclose a stamped self-addressed envelope when writing and respect the privacy of individuals. This book does not grant or imply any permission whatsoever to enter premises to look at old buses except by the agreement of the group involved. Note that, where buses are licensed for use on public passenger-carrying services, the use of individual vehicles will vary from time to time, as the demands of their preservation dictate.

Whilst some of the restored vehicles detailed here have been 'officially' preserved by their former operators, the majority have been restored and conserved by volunteers, often working in difficult conditions with limited resources of time, money and materials. That there are so many buses and coaches fully restored is a testimony to the dedication of bus enthusiasts over the last 40 years or more, and it is intended that the vehicles will have a long and secure future.

The information used in this book is as provided by the organisations listed, for which the authors express their thanks. As far as possible, details are correct to 30 September 2001. Any information on further collections not included in the current edition will be most welcome. If you own vehicles, or are associated with such an organisation, please contact NARTM at the address given on page 8.

Left:
Visitor RTW29 of the RTW Bus Group stands alongside Cobham Bus Museum's resident RM3.
Philip Lamb

Right:
A new addition at the City of Portsmouth Preserved Transport Depot is Leyland National 2 Portsmouth 100 (CPO 100W).
Philip Lamb

For each vehicle, details given include the present registration number, year first registered, brief chassis and body details (including seating) and original operator. Standard PSV Circle body codes are used, as outlined below.

Body type (before seating capacity):
A   articulated
B   single-deck bus
C   coach (single-deck)
CH   double-decker coach
Ch   charabanc
CO   convertible open-top double-decker
DP   dual-purpose (eg coach seats in bus shell)
F   full-front (where not normal for chassis)
H   Highbridge double-decker
L   Lowbridge double-decker (ie with sunken side gangway upstairs; all other types — with conventional gangways — are 'H', regardless of overall height)
O   open-top double-decker
OB   open-top single-decker
PO   partially-open-top double decker
R   single-decker with raised rear saloon (eg over luggage compartment)
T   Toastrack
U   Utility body

Seating capacity:
For double-deckers this is shown with the upper-deck capacity first, eg 43/31

Door position (after seating capacity):
C   centre entrance/exit
D   dual doors (usually front entrance and centre exit)
F   front or forward entrance/exit
R   open rear platform
RD   rear entrance/exit with doors
RO   open rear platform with open staircase
T   triple doors (eg on articulated vehicles)

Suffix:
t   fitted with toilet
l   fitted with wheelchair lift

The restoration state is given in accordance with the following code:
R   restored;
RP   restoration in progress;
A   awaiting restoration.

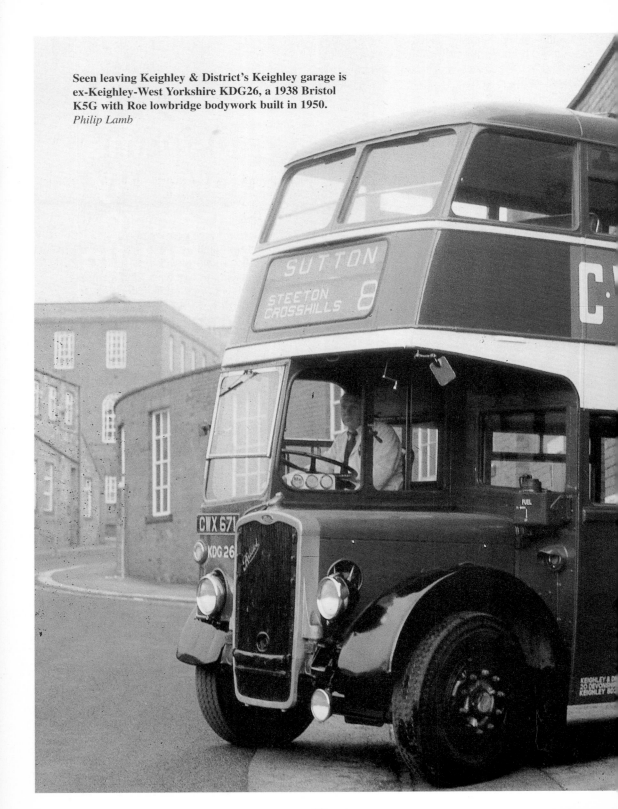

Seen leaving Keighley & District's Keighley garage is ex-Keighley-West Yorkshire KDG26, a 1938 Bristol K5G with Roe lowbridge bodywork built in 1950. *Philip Lamb*

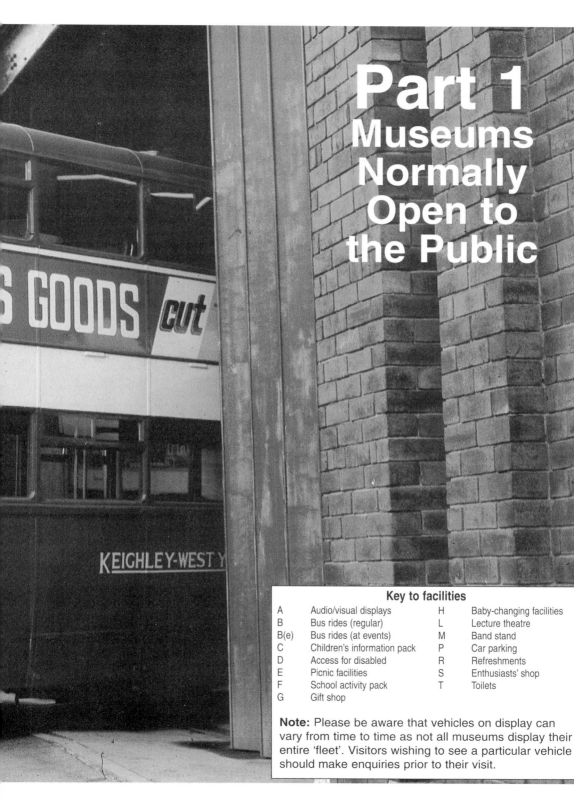

Part 1
Museums Normally Open to the Public

S GOODS cut

KEIGHLEY-WEST Y

Key to facilities

A	Audio/visual displays	H	Baby-changing facilities
B	Bus rides (regular)	L	Lecture theatre
B(e)	Bus rides (at events)	M	Band stand
C	Children's information pack	P	Car parking
D	Access for disabled	R	Refreshments
E	Picnic facilities	S	Enthusiasts' shop
F	School activity pack	T	Toilets
G	Gift shop		

Note: Please be aware that vehicles on display can vary from time to time as not all museums display their entire 'fleet'. Visitors wishing to see a particular vehicle should make enquiries prior to their visit.

Abbey Pumping Station Leicester

Contact address: Corporation Road, Leicester LE4 5PX
Phone: 0116 299 5111
Fax: 0116 299 5125
Brief description: The Museum is a Victorian pumping-station dating from 1892 with four beam-engines. The vehicle collection is on view on special open days. On these occasions, one of the beam-engines is steamed.
Events planned: Please see the enthusiast press for details.
Opening days/times:
Mon-Sat: 10.00 to 16.00 (17.00 in summer)
Sun: 14.00 to 16.30 (17.00 in summer)

Directions by car: A6 (north of Leicester) joins Abbey Lane at Redhill Island. Corporation Road is off Abbey Lane.
Directions by public transport: From City Centre (Charles Street) take bus 54 to top of Corporation Road.
Charges: Free except on special open days.
Facilities: C D E G H P R (on open days) T

Registration	Date	Chassis	Body	New to	Fleet No	Status
CBC 921	1939	AEC Renown O664	Northern Counties H32/32R	Leicester City Transport	329	R
GAY 171	1950	Leyland Tiger PS1/1	Willowbrook DP35F	Allen of Mountsorrel	43	A
MTL 750	1958	Leyland Tiger Cub PSUC1/2	Yeates DP43F	Delaine Coaches of Bourne	47	R
TBC 164	1958	Leyland Titan PD3/1	Willowbrook H41/33R	Leicester City Transport	164	R
JMC 121K	1972	AEC Reliance 6MU4R	Plaxton C34C	Glenton Tours of London	121	R
OUM 727P	1976	Bedford J2SZ10	Caetano C16F	Anderton Tours of Keighley		R
B401 NJF	1984	Ford Transit 190D	Rootes B16F	Midland Fox	M1	R

Notes:

CBC 921	On view at Snibston Discovery Park
GAY 171	In store at Snibston Discovery Park

Amberley Museum

Contact address: Amberley, Arundel, West Sussex, BN18 9LT
Phone: 01798 831370
Fax: 01798 831831
E-mail: office@amberleymuseum.co.uk
Brief Description: The industrial museum has a wide range of attractions, including rail and bus operations. Some buses in the collection are museum-owned and others are owned by the Southdown Omnibus Trust or are in private hands.
Events planned: 15 September 2002 — Bus event (please see enthusiast press for details).

Opening days/times:
March to October: Weds to Sun (also Mon and Tues during school holidays)
Directions by car: Situated close to Amberley railway station on the B2139. Approach from the north and west via the A29 and from the east via the A24 and A283.
Directions by public transport: Hourly rail service calls at Amberley station which is adjacent to the museum.
Charges: Details not finalised at time of publication.
Facilities: A B B(e) C D E F G H L P R T

Registration	Date	Chassis	Body	New to	Fleet No	Status
IB 552	1914	Tilling Stevens TS3 Petrol Electric	Newman O22/16R	Worthing Motor Services		R
CD 5125	1920	Leyland N	Short O27/24R	Southdown Motor Services	125	R
CD 4867	1923	Tilling Stevens TS3A Petrol Electric	(chassis only)			RP
BP 9822	1924	Shelvoke & Drewery Freighter	Hickman (replica) B18F	Tramocar of Worthing		R
MO 9324	1927	Tilling Stevens B9A	Brush B32R	Thames Valley Traction Co	152	R
UF 1517	1927	Dennis 30cwt	Short B19R	Southdown Motor Services	517	R
BR 7132	1929	Leyland Lion LT1	Leyland B34F	Sunderland Corporation	2	R
UF 6473	1930	Leyland Titan TD1	Leyland H24/24R	Southdown Motor Services	873	R
UF 6805	1930	Tilling Stevens B10A2	Short B31R	Southdown Motor Services	1205	RP
UF 7428	1931	Leyland Titan TD1	Short H26/24R	Southdown Motor Services	928	R
EUF 184	1938	Leyland Titan TD5	Leyland -	Southdown Motor Services	0184	A

Notes:

IB 552	Petrol-electric Transmission. Body new 1909.
CD 5125	Restored using a P or Q 5- or 6-ton chassis. Rebodied 1928
CD 4867	Petrol-electric. To be restored as Southdown replica
BP 9822	Solid tyres. Replica body built at Amberley
UF 1517	All-metal body.

MO 9324	Mechanical Transmission. Restored at Amberley
UF 6805	Mechanical Transmission.
EUF 184	Converted from bus 184; fitted with breakdown vehicle body ex Leyland TD1 872 (UF 6472)

Above:

Former Glenton Tours 121, an AEC Reliance with Plaxton centre-entrance coachwork is part of a small collection of buses and coaches at Abbey Pumping Station, Leicester. *Philip Lamb*

Right:

One of the oldest buses in regular use is Amberley Museum's ex-Thames Valley 152, a 1927 Brush-bodied Tilling Stevens B9A. It is seen here at Worthing. *D. J. Smith*

Aston Manor Road Transport Museum

Contact address: The Old Tram Depot, 208-216 Witton Lane, Aston, Birmingham B6 6QE
Phone: 0121 322 2298
Fax: 0121 308 0544
Affiliation: NARTM
Brief description: The 19th-century former tram depot houses a selection of buses, coaches, commercial vehicles and tramcar bodies in an authentic setting — the depot still has tram tracks and stone sets in situ. There are also many small exhibits, working model layouts and video presentations.

Events planned:
26 May 2002 — Two Museums Running Day. Bus service linking Aston Manor and Wythall.
14 July 2002 — Open day/vehicle gathering.
15 Sept 2002 — Outer Circle Rally at Cannon Hill Park.
24 Nov 2002 — Collectors' fair with free bus rides.
Please see the enthusiast press for other events.

Opening days/times:
Saturdays, Sundays and Bank Hols 11.00 to 17.00. Other times by arrangement.
Opening times may vary during September and over Christmas/New Year period.
Directions by car: Easy access from M6 junction 6.
Directions by public transport: Rail to Witton Station and a short walk (170yd)
Bus No 7 from Birmingham City Centre or bus No 11, outer circle to Witton Square.
Charges:
Adults £1, Child 50p, Family £2.75.
Admission charges may vary on special event days.
Facilities: A B(e) D P R S T
Other information: Not all of the vehicles listed are on display at the museum. To view any vehicle not normally accessible, visitors should enquire at the museum as to arrangements for viewing.

Registration	Date	Chassis	Body	New to	Fleet No	Status
note z	1925	AEC S	Buckingham	Birmingham Corporation Tramways	215	A
OP 237	1926	(body only)	Short H32/26R	Birmingham Corporation Tramways	208	A
EA 4181	1929	Dennis E	Dixon B32F	West Bromwich Corporation	32	RP
HA 4963	1930	SOS RR	Brush	BMMO ('Midland Red')	963	A
JF 2378	1931	AEC Regal 662	Burlingham C32R	Provincial of Leicester	R1	R
note x	1931	SOS IM4	(chassis only)	BMMO ('Midland Red')		RP
OJ 9347	1933	Morris Commercial Dictator	Metro Cammell B—F	Birmingham Corporation Tramways	47	A
ANB 851	1934	Crossley Mancunian	Crossley/MCT H28/26R	Manchester Corporation	436	RP
AOG 679	1935	Daimler COG5	-	Birmingham Corporation Tramways	83	RP
CDH 501	1935	Dennis Lance	Park Royal H28/24R	Walsall Corporation	110	A
EHA 775	1938	SOS SON	English Electric -	BMMO ('Midland Red')	2207	A
FON 630	1942	Leyland Titan TD7	(chassis only)	Birmingham City Transport	1330	A
DDM 652	1946	Maudslay Marathon II	Duple C33F	Rhyl United Coachways		R
KTT 689	1948	Guy Vixen	Wadham FC29F	Court Cars of Tourquay		R
JHA 890	1949	BMMO S8	Metro Cammell B40F	BMMO ('Midland Red')	3290	A
GUJ 608	1950	Sentinel STC4	Sentinel B40F	Sentinal demonstrator		R
JOJ 222	1950	Leyland Titan PD2/1	Park Royal H29/25R	Birmingham City Transport	2222	RP
JOJ 257	1950	Leyland Tiger PS2	Weymann B34F	Birmingham City Transport	2257	A
JOJ 526	1950	Guy Arab IV	Metro Cammell H30/24R	Birmingham City Transport	2526	A
JOJ 548	1950	Guy Arab IV	Metro Cammell H30/24R	Birmingham City Transport	2548	RP
KEL 131	1950	Leyland Titan PD2/3	Weymann FH33/25D	Bournemouth Corporation	131	RP
KHA 352	1950	BMMO CL2	Plaxton C26C	BMMO ('Midland Red')	3352	RP
SB 8155	1950	Guy Wolf	Ormac B20F	Alexander MacConnacher of Ballachulish		R
MLL 584	1951	AEC Regal IV 9821LT RF	Metro Cammell B37F	London Transport	RF 197	R
JOJ 847	1952	Daimler CVG6	Crossley H30/25RD	Birmingham City Transport	2847	A
LLU 613	1952	AEC Regent III O961 RT	Weymann H30/26R	London Transport	RT 3254	RP
LOG 301	1952	Guy Arab IV	Saunders Roe H30/25R	Birmingham City Transport	3001	RP
LOG 302	1954	Daimler CLG5	Metro Cammell H30/25R	Birmingham City Transport	3002	R
MOF 90	1954	Guy Arab IV	Metro Cammell H30/25R	Birmingham City Transport	3090	RP
RRU 903	1955	Leyland Tiger Cub PSUC1/1	Park Royal B40F	Bournemouth Corporation	266	RP
773 FHA	1958	BMMO D9	BMMO H40/32RD	BMMO ('Midland Red')	4773	A
1294 RE	1959	Guy Arab LUF	Burlingham C41F	Harper Bros of Heath Hayes	60	A
WLT 506	1960	AEC Routemaster R2RH	Park Royal H36/28R	London Transport	RM 506	RP
264 ERY	1963	Leyland Titan PD3A/1	Park Royal O41/33R	Leicester City Transport	264	R
3035 HA	1963	BMMO D9	BMMO O40/32RD	BMMO ('Midland Red')	5035	RP
334 CRW	1963	Daimler CVG6	Metro Cammell H34/29R	Coventry City Transport	334	RP
6314 HA	1963	BMMO D9	BMMO H40/32RD	BMMO ('Midland Red')	5314	A
966 RVO	1963	Bedford VAL 14	Yeates C50D	Barton Transport of Chilwell	966	R

Ex-Coventry 334, the City's penultimate half-cab double-decker is currently undergoing a lengthy restoration at Aston Manor Road Transport Museum. No 334 is a 1963 Metro-Cammell-bodied Daimler CVG6.
Philip Lamb

Registration	Date	Chassis	Body	New to	Fleet No	Status
436 KOV	1964	Daimler Fleetline CRG6LX	Park Royal H43/33F	Birmingham City Transport	3436	A
6370 HA	1964	BMMO D9	BMMO H40/32RD	BMMO ('Midland Red')	5370	R
EHA 415D	1966	BMMO D9	BMMO/Willowbrook H40/32RD	BMMO ('Midland Red')	5415	R
KOX 663F	1967	AEC Swift MP2R	MCW B37D	Birmingham City Transport	3663	RP
LHA 870F	1967	BMMO S21	BMMO DP49F	BMMO ('Midland Red')	5870	R
UHA 969H	1970	BMMO S23	BMMO/Plaxton B51F	BMMO ('Midland Red')	5969	A
XNX 136H	1970	Leyland Leopard	Alexander DP49F	Stratford-upon-Avon Blue Motors	36	R
XON 41J	1971	Daimler Fleetline CRG6LX	Park Royal H43/33F	West Midlands PTE	4041	R
HFL 672L	1973	Leyland Atlantean AN68/2R	Northern Counties H47/34F	Whippet Coaches of Fenstanton		R
OFR 989M	1974	AEC Swift	Marshall B47D	Blackpool Corporation	589	RP
JOV 714P	1976	Bristol VRTSL2/6LX	MCW H43/33F	West Midlands PTE	4714	R
OAS 287R	1977	Leyland National	Leyland National DP45F	West Midlands PTE	6825	RP
OOX 816R	1977	Leyland National	Leyland National DP45F	West Midlands PTE	6816	A
WDA 700T	1979	Leyland Fleetline FE30AGR	MCW H43/33F	West Midlands PTE	7000	R
F685 YOG	1988	MCW Metrorider MF150/113	MCW B23F	West Midlands PTE	685	RP

Notes:

note z	Registration not known
note x	Registration not known
OJ 9347	Renumbered 77 in 1935
ANB 851	Rebodied 1938
AOG 679	Originally bus 679 with Northern Counties H26/22R body; rebodied 1947 as a van
KHA 352	Rebodied 1963
KEL 131	Built with twin staircases and dual doors
LOG 302	Chrome-plated chassis exhibited 1952 Commercial Motor Show
RRU 903	Converted for OMO and rear door removed in 1957
3035 HA	Originally H40/32RD; converted to open-top by Marshall ('Obsolete Fleet') London (OM6)
264 ERY	Originally H41/33R

A rare petrol-engined Maudslay Marathon II, DDM 652, with Duple coachwork, is restored in the livery of Prairie Coaches.
Philip Lamb

Birmingham & Midland Museum of Transport   Wythall

Contact address: Chapel Lane, Wythall, Worcestershire, B47 6JX
Phone: 01564 826471
E-mail: enquiries@bammot.org.uk
Web site: www.bammot.org.uk
Brief description: The collection is based on buses built and/or operated locally, plus others of significant PSV history. In addition, there is a unique collection of battery-operated road vehicles and a miniature passenger-carrying steam railway on site.
Events planned: Please see the enthusiast press for details, generally Bank Holidays or last Sunday of summer and autumn months. Special enthusiast days 26 May, 26 August, 27 October 2002
Opening days/times: Saturdays, Sundays and Bank Holidays 11.00 to 17.00, Easter Sunday to end of October.

Directions by car: Wythall is on the main A435 Birmingham-Evesham road. The museum is next to Wythall old church. From M42 use junction 3 and head towards Birmingham.
Directions by public transport: Museum services operate on event days.
First Midland Red serves Wythall from Birmingham; Travel West Midlands from Solihull. Neither operates on Sundays
Wythall rail station is 25min walk from museum.
Charges: £1.50 but higher charges apply on event days (generally £3).
Facilities: B(e) E P S T
Other information: Refreshments available on event days

Registration	Date	Chassis	Body	New to	Fleet No	Status
O 9926	1913	Tilling Stevens TTA2	Thomas Tilling O18/16RO	BMMO ('Midland Red')	26	RP
HA 3501	1925	SOS Standard	Ransomes Sims & Jefferies B32F	BMMO ('Midland Red')	501	A
CN 2870	1927	SOS Q	Brush B37F	Northern General Transport Co	321	RP
CC 7745	1928	SOS QL	Brush B37F	Royal Blue of Llandudno		A
OV 4090	1931	Morris Commercial Dictator	Metro Cammell B34F	Birmingham Corporation Tramways	90	A
OV 4486	1931	AEC Regent 661	Metro Cammell H27/21R	Birmingham Corporation Tramways	486	A
OC 527	1933	Morris Commercial Imperial	Metro Cammell H50R	Birmingham Corporation Tramways	527	A
AHA 582	1935	SOS DON	Brush B36F	BMMO ('Midland Red')	1703	A
CVP 207	1937	Daimler COG5	Metro Cammell H30/24R	Birmingham City Transport	1107	R
RC 4615	1937	AEC Regal 0662	Willowbrook B34F	Trent Motor Traction Co	714	R
GHA 337	1940	SOS SON	Brush B38F	BMMO ('Midland Red')	2418	RP
HHA 637	1946	BMMO S6	Metro Cammell B40F	BMMO ('Midland Red')	3036	A
FFY 402	1947	Leyland Titan PD2/3	Leyland O30/26R	Southport Corporation	85	RP
GUE 247	1948	Leyland Tiger PS1	Northern Coach Builders B34F	Stratford-upon-Avon Blue Motors	41	A
HOV 685	1948	Leyland Titan PD2/1	Brush H30/24R	Birmingham City Transport	1685	R
JRR 404	1948	Leyland Titan PD1	Duple L29/26F	Barton Transport of Chilwell	473	RP
JXC 432	1948	AEC Regent III O961 RT	Weymann H30/26R	London Transport	RT 624	A
KAL 579	1948	Daimler CVD6	Massey H33/28RD	W Gash & Sons of Newark	DD2	R
FDM 724	1949	Foden PVD6	Massey H30/26R	E H Phillips Motor Services of Holywell		A
FJW 616+	1949	Sunbeam F4	Park Royal H28/26R	Wolverhampton Corporation	616	A
HDG 448	1949	Albion Venturer CX19	Metro Cammell H30/26R	Cheltenham District Traction Co	72	R
HWO 334	1949	Guy Arab III	Duple L27/26R	Red & White Services	34	R
JOJ 245	1950	Leyland Tiger PS2/1	Weymann B34F	Birmingham City Transport	2245	RP
JOJ 533	1950	Guy Arab IV	Metro Cammell H30/24R	Birmingham City Transport	2533	R
JUE 349	1950	Leyland Tiger PS2/3	Northern Counties H35/28F	Stratford-upon-Avon Blue Motors	33	RP
KFM 775	1950	Bristol L5G	ECW B35R	Crosville Motor Services	KG126	R
NHA 744	1950	BMMO S12	Brush B44F	BMMO ('Midland Red')	3744	RP
NHA 795	1950	BMMO D5B	Brush H30/26RD	BMMO ('Midland Red')	3795	A
ORB 277	1950	Daimler CVD6	Duple C35F	Tailby & George ('Blue Bus Services') Willington		R
MXX 23	1952	AEC Regal IV 9821LT RF	Metro Cammell B41F	London Transport	RF 381	R
JOJ 976	1953	Guy Arab IV	Metro Cammell H30/25R	Birmingham City Transport	2976	R
PDH 808	1953	Leyland Royal Tiger PSU1	Park Royal DP40F	Walsall Corporation	808	R
RDH 505	1953	Leyland Titan PD2/12	Roe FH33/23RD	Walsall Corporation	815	A
SHA 431	1953	Leyland Titan PD2/12	Leyland H30/26RD	BMMO ('Midland Red')	4031	RP
FRC 956	1954	Leyland Titan PD2/12	Leyland H32/26RD	Trent Motor Traction Co	1256	R
UHA 255	1955	BMMO S14	BMMO B44F	BMMO ('Midland Red')	4255	A
XHA 482	1956	BMMO D7	Metro Cammell H37/26RD	BMMO ('Midland Red')	4482	R
XHA 496	1956	BMMO D7	Metro Cammell	BMMO ('Midland Red')	4496	A
SUK 3	1957	Guy Arab IV	Metro Cammell H33/27R	Wolverhampton Corporation	3	A
UTU 596J	1957	Guy Otter NLLODP	Mulliner B26F	Douglas Corporation	9	A

Left:
Seen visiting the Black Country Living Museum is BaMMOT's 1953 Metro-Cammell-bodied Guy Arab IV, Birmingham 2976.
Philip Lamb

Below:
Cheltenham District 6037 is an ECW-bodied Bristol FSF6G. Dating from 1961, it has been preserved at Wythall for some years.
BaMMOT

Note: Please be aware that vehicles on display can vary from time to time as not all museums display their entire 'fleet'. Visitors wishing to see a particular vehicle should make enquiries prior to their visit.

Registration	Date	Chassis	Body	New to	Fleet No	Status
HFO 742	1958	Albion Victor FT39	Reading B35F	Guernsey Railway Co	62	R
VVP 911	1958	Bedford SB3	Duple C41F	Sandwell Motor Co of Birmingham		R
WDF 569	1959	Leyland Tiger Cub PSUC1	Willowbrook DP41F	Soudley Valley Coaches of Cinderford		R
871 KHA	1960	BMMO D9	BMMO H40/32RD	BMMO ('Midland Red')	4871	A
943 KHA	1960	BMMO D10	BMMO H43/35F	BMMO ('Midland Red')	4943	R
802 MHW	1961	Bristol Lodekka FSF6G	ECW H34/26F	Cheltenham District Traction Co	6037	R
3016 HA	1962	BMMO D9	BMMO/LPC O40/32RD	BMMO ('Midland Red')	5016	R
5073 HA	1962	BMMO S15	BMMO B40F	BMMO ('Midland Red')	5073	R
248 NEA	1963	Daimler CVG6-30	Metro Cammell H41/33R	West Bromwich Corporation	248	R
6545 HA	1964	BMMO S16	BMMO B52F	BMMO ('Midland Red')	5545	R
BHA 399C	1965	BMMO D9	BMMO H40/32RD	BMMO ('Midland Red')	5399	R
BHA 656C	1965	BMMO CM6T	BMMO C44Ft	BMMO ('Midland Red')	5656	R
BON 474C	1965	Daimler Fleetline CRG6LX	Marshall B37F	Birmingham City Transport	3474	R
CUV 219C	1965	AEC Routemaster R2RH/1	Park Royal CH36/29RD	London Transport	RCL 2219	R
EHA 767D	1966	BMMO S17	BMMO/Plaxton B52F	BMMO ('Midland Red')	5767	R
GHA 415D	1966	Daimler Fleetline CRG6LX	Alexander H44/33F	BMMO ('Midland Red')	6015	RP
GRY 60D	1966	Leyland Titan PD3A/1	Park Royal H41/33R	Leicester City Transport	60	R
HBF 679D	1966	Leyland Titan PD2A/27	Metro Cammell H36/28RD	Harper Bros of Heath Hayes	27	RP
JHA 868E	1967	BMMO S21	BMMO DP49F	BMMO ('Midland Red')	5868	R
KHW 306E	1967	Bristol RELL6L	ECW B53F	Cheltenham District Traction Co	1000	R
NJW 719E	1967	Daimler Roadliner SRC6	Strachan B54D	Wolverhampton Corporation	719	R
KOX 780F	1968	Daimler Fleetline CRG6LX	Park Royal H43/33F	Birmingham City Transport	3780	R
NEA 101F	1968	Daimler Fleetline CRG6LX	Metro Cammell H42/31F	West Bromwich Corporation	101	A
XDH 56G	1968	Daimler Fleetline CRC6-36	Northern Counties H51/34D	Walsall Corporationl	56	RP
OTA 632G	1969	Bristol RELH6G	ECW C45F	Southern National Omnibus Co (Royal Blue)	1460	R
SHA 645G	1969	Leyland Leopard PSU4A/4R	Plaxton C36F	BMMO ('Midland Red')	6145	R
UHA 956H	1969	BMMO S23	BMMO/Plaxton B51F	BMMO ('Midland Red')	5956	R
XDH 516G	1969	Daimler Fleetline CRG6LX	Northern Counties H41/27D	Walsall Corporation	116	R
FRB 211H	1970	Bristol VRTSL2/6LX	ECW H39/31F	Midland General Omnibus Co	322	R
UHA 981H	1970	BMMO S23	BMMO/Plaxton B51F	BMMO ('Midland Red')	5981	R
WNG 864H	1970	Bristol RELL6G	ECW DP50F	Eastern Counties Omnibus Co	RLE 864	R
CBD 778K	1972	Bristol VRTSL2/6LX	ECW H39/31F	United Counties Omnibus Co	778	R
OWE 271K	1972	Bristol VRTSL2/6LX	East Lancs H43/30F	Sheffield Transport	271	RP
TCH 274L	1973	Bristol RELH6G	ECW DP49F	Midland General Omnibus Co	274	R
PHA 370M	1974	Ford R1014	Plaxton/Midland Red DP23F	Midland Red Omnibus Co	370	A
JOV 613P	1975	Daimler Fleetline CRG6LX	Park Royal H43/33F	West Midlands PTE	4613	R
99-64-HB	1976	Den Oudsten LOK	Den Oudsten B35D	VAD of Ermele (Netherlands)	5656	A
KON 311P	1976	Leyland Fleetline FE30 ALR	Metro Cammell H43/33F	West Midlands PTE	6311	R
NOE 544R	1976	Leyland National 11351A/1R	Leyland National B49F	Midland Red Omnibus Co	544	RP
BOK 1V	1979	MCW Metrobus DR102/12	MCW H43/30F	West Midlands PTE	2001	A
KVF 247V +trolleybus	1980	Bristol VRTSL3/6LXB	ECW H43/31F	Eastern Counties Omnibus Co	VR 247	RP

Notes:

RC 4615	Rebodied 1950
FFY 402	Originally H30/26R
KAL 579	Rebodied 1958
JUE 349	Rebodied 1963
XHA 496	Converted to Breakdown Vehicle 1972
UTU 596J	Originally registered WMN 485
HFO 742	Originally registered 8231
943 KHA	Entered service 1961
3016 HA	Originally H40/32RD; converted to open-top by Marshall ('Obsolete Fleet') London (OM5)
5073 HA	Reseated from DP40F in 1969
CBD 778K	Modified to resemble VRTSL3 by United Counties
PHA 370M	Shortened by Midland Red in 1979
99-64-HB	Netherlands registration
KON 311P	Gardner engine fitted in 1981

Black Country Living Museum   Dudley

Contact address: Tipton Road, Dudley, West Midlands DY1 4SQ
Phone: 0121 557 9643
Brief description: Tramway operation daily. Trollybus operation on Sundays and Bank Holidays.
Events planned: Trolleybus 2002 — 1-16 June, visiting trolleybuses running every day
Opening days/times: Summer: daily 10.00-17.00. Winter: Wednesdays to Sundays 10.00-16.00. Some evening openings

Directions by car: M5 (jct2) signposted on Motorway. follow signs on A4123 to 'Black Country Living Museum'.
Directions by public transport: Central Trains to Tipton station. Travel West Midlands 224, 263, 270, 311-313 to Museum.
Facilities: A, B, B(e)C, D, E, F, G, H, L, P, R, T
Contact (transport Group): Black Country Museum Transport Group, 28 Farm Close, Etchinghill, Rugeley, Staffs WS15 2XT.

Registration	Date	Chassis	Body	New to	Fleet No	Status
UK 9978+	1931	Guy BTX	Guy H—/—R	Wolverhampton Corporation	78	A
DUK 833+	1946	Sunbeam W	Roe H32/28R	Wolverhampton Corporation	433	R
FEA156	1949	Daimler CVG5	Metro Cammell B38R	West Bromwich Corporation	156	RP
GEA 174	1952	Daimler CVG6	Weymann H30/26R	West Bromwich Corporation	174	R
TDH 912+	1955	Sunbeam F4A	Willowbrook H36/34RD	Walsall Corporation	862	R
SCH 237+	1960	Sunbeam F4A	Roe H37/28R	Derby Corporation	237	R
GHA 327D	1965	Leyland Leopard PSU4/4R	Plaxton	Midland Red Omnibus Co	5827	R
XDH 519G	1969	Daimler Fleetline CRG6LX	Northern Counties H41/27D	Walsall Corporation	119	RP

+trolleybus

Note:
DUK 833   Rebodied in 1959
GHA 327D   Converted to breakdown vehicle in 1979.

Bristol Aero Collection   Kemble

Contact address: William Staniforth 37 Corbett Road, Hollywood, Birmingham B47 5LP (SAE please)
E-mail: william.staniforth@Virgin.net
Affiliation: NARTM
Location: Hangar A1, Kemble Airfield, Nr Cirencester, Gloucs GL7 6BA
Brief description: A display of Bristol buses housed in an aircraft

hangar alongside a Bristol aircraft and other products from the companies originally founded by Sir George White.
Events planned: 4 August 2002 — Kemble Steam Gathering, traction engine rally and special display of Bristol buses, lorries and cars etc.
Opening days/times: Sundays and Bank Holiday Mondays, Easter to end of October, 10.00-16.00. Private parties by arrangement.

Registration	Date	Chassis	Body	New to	Fleet No	Status
HW 6634	1929	Bristol B	(chassis only)	Bristol Tramways		A
KHW 630	1948	Leyland Titan PD1	ECW H30/26R	Bristol Tramways	C4019	A
JEL 257	1949	Bristol K5G	ECW L27/28R	Hants & Dorset Motor Services	1238	A
LHW 918	1949	Bristol L5G	ECW B35R	Bristol Tramways	2410	A
MHU 49	1949	Bedford OB	Duple B30F	Bristol Tramways	207	RP
GAM 216	1950	Bristol L6B/PA	ECW C32R	Wilts & Dorset	297	A
LFM 753	1950	Bristol L6B	ECW DP31R	Crosville Motor Services	KW172	R
CNH 699	1952	Bristol KSW6B	ECW L27/28R	United Counties Omnibus Co	860	A
NFM 67	1952	Bristol KSW6B	ECW H32/28R	Crosville Motor Services	MW435	A
UHY 359	1955	Bristol KSW6B	ECW H32/28R	Bristol Tramways	C8319	A
YHT 958	1958	Bristol Lodekka LD6B	ECW O33/25RD	Bristol Omnibus Co	L8462	R
980 DAE	1959	Bristol MW5G	ECW B45F	Bristol Omnibus Co	2960	A
904 OFM	1960	Bristol SC4LK	ECW C33F	Crosville Motor Services	CSG655	RP
Q507 OHR	1961	Bristol MW6G	ECW	Bristol Omnibus Co	W151	RP
507 OHU	1962	Bristol Lodekka FLF6G	ECW H38/32F	Bristol Omnibus Co	7062	RP
862 RAE	1962	Bristol SUS4A	ECW B30F	Bristol Omnibus Co	301	R
RDB 872	1964	Dennis Loline III	Alexander H39/32F	North Western Road Car Co	872	RP
BHU 92C	1965	Bristol MW6G	ECW DP43F	Bristol Omnibus Co	2428	R
CWN 629C	1965	Bristol MW6G	ECW B45F	United Welsh Services	134	A
DFE 963D	1966	Bristol Lodekka FS5G	ECW H33/27RD	Lincolnshire Road Car Co	2537	R
FHT 15D	1966	Bristol Lodekka FLF6G	ECW	Bristol Omnibus Co	7240	RP

Registration	Date	Chassis	Body	New to	Fleet No	Status
LRN 60J	1970	Bristol VRLLH6L	ECW CH42/18Ct	W C Standerwick	60	R
GYC 160K	1971	Bristol LH6L	ECW B45F	Hutchings & Cornelius Services of South Petherton		RP
PUO 331M	1974	Bristol LH6L	Plaxton C41F	Western National Omnibus Co (Royal Blue)	1331	RP
HAX 399N	1975	Bristol LHS6L	Duple C35F	R I Davies & Son of Tredegar		RP
KHU 326P	1976	Bristol LH6L	ECW B43F	Bristol Omnibus Co	376	RP
KOU 791P	1976	Bristol VRTSL3/6LXB	ECW H39/31F	Bristol Omnibus Co	5505	RP
TWS 910T	1979	Bristol VRTSL3/6LXB	ECW H43/27D	Bristol Omnibus Co	5129	R
AHW 200V	1980	Bristol VRTSL3/6LXB	ECW H43/27D	Bristol Omnibus Co	5149	RP

Notes:

YHT 958	Originally H33/25RD
Q507 OHR	Originally coach 2111 registered 404 LHT; converted to breakdown vehicle in 1974
507 OHU	On display at Aston Manor Road Transport Museum
FHT 15D	Ex playbus; to become exhibition vehicle

A well-known member of the Bristol Aero Collection is former Bristol Greyhound Bristol MW6G 2428.
Philip Lamb

British Commercial Vehicle Museum — Leyland

Contact address: King Street, Leyland, Lancashire, PR5 2LE
Phone: 01772 451011
Fax: 01772 623404
Brief description: A unique line-up of historic commercial vehicles and buses spans a century of truck and bus building. More than 50 exhibits are on display in this national collection.
Events planned: Please see the enthusiast press for details.
Opening days/times:
April to end of September: Sundays, Tuesdays, Wednesdays and Bank Holidays, 10.00 to 17.00

October: Sundays only, 10.00 to 17.00
Directions by car: Close to the M6 Junction 28.
Directions by public transport:
By train to Leyland station (on West Coast main line).
Buses from Preston and Chorley bus stations.
Charges: Adult £4, Child/OAP £2, Family £10.
Facilities: A B(e) D F G L P R S T

Registration	Date	Chassis	Body	New to	Fleet No	Status
XW 9892	1925	Tilling Stevens TS7	Tilling B30R	Thomas Tilling		R
KYY 653	1950	AEC Regent III O961 RT	Weymann H30/26R	London Transport	RT 1798	R
XTC 684	1955	Leyland LFDD	Metro Cammell H37/24RD	Leyland Demonstrator		A
OED 217	1956	Foden PVD6	East Lancs H30/28R	Warrington Corporation	112	R
301 LJ+	1962	Sunbeam MF2B	Weymann H37/28D	Bournemouth Corporation	301	R
UTC 768D	1966	Leyland Leopard	Plaxton C43F	Lancashire United Transport	216	R

+ Trolleybus

Castle Point Transport Museum — Canvey Island

Contact address: 105 Point Road, Canvey Island, Essex SS8 7TP
Phone: 01268 684272
Affiliation: NARTM
Brief description: This historic former Canvey & District bus depot, built in 1935, houses approximately 35 commercial vehicles spanning the years 1944 to 1988. Exhibits include buses, coaches, lorries, fire engines and military vehicles. They can be seen in varying stages from the totally restored to those in need of complete restoration. Completely run by volunteers, membership of the society is available at £6 per annum.

Events planned: Please see enthusiast press for details
Opening days/times: Open on Sundays, mid April to mid October.
Directions by car: A130 to Canvey Island; follow brown tourism signs on reaching the island.
Directions by public transport: By rail to South Benfleet, then by bus to Leigh Beck, Canvey Island.
Charges: Free admission. Donations welcome. A charge is made on the Transport Show day in October.
Facilities: B(e) P T
Other information: Hot drinks available.

Registration	Date	Chassis	Body	New to	Fleet No	Status
FOP 429	1944	Daimler CWA6	Duple O33/26R	Birmingham Corporation Tramways	1429	R
JVW 430	1944	Bristol K5G	ECW L27/28R	Eastern National Omnibus Co	3885	R
MPU 52	1947	Leyland Titan PD1A	ECW L27/26R	Eastern National Omnibus Co	3991	RP
CFV 851	1948	Bedford OB	Duple C29F	Seagull Coaches of Blackpool		R
LHY 937	1949	Bristol K6B	ECW H31/28R	Bristol Tramways	C3448	RP
LYR 997	1949	AEC Regent III O961 RT	Weymann H30/26R	London Transport	RT 2827	R
NEH 453	1949	Leyland Titan OPD2/1	Northern Counties L27/26RD	Potteries Motor Traction Co	L453	R
ONO 49	1950	Bristol L5G	ECW B35R	Eastern National Omnibus Co	4029	R
PTW 110	1950	Bristol L6B	ECW FC31F	Eastern National Omnibus Co	4107	RP
VRF 372	1951	Foden PVRF6	Harrington C41C	Bassett's Coaches of Tittenson		RP
WNO 478	1953	Bristol KSW5G	ECW O33/28R	Westcliff-on-Sea Motor Services		R
JAP 698	1954	Harrington Contender	Harrington C41C	Audawn Coaches of Corringham		RP
XVX 19	1954	Bristol Lodekka LD5G	ECW H33/25R	Eastern National Omnibus Co	4208	R
381 BKM	1957	AEC Reliance MU3RV	Harrington C41F	Maidstone & District Motor Services	C381	RP
PHJ 954	1958	Leyland Titan PD3/6	Massey L35/32R	Southend Corporation	315	RP
217 MHK	1959	Bristol MW6G	ECW DP41F	Eastern National Omnibus Co	480	R
236 LNO	1959	Bristol Lodekka LDL6LX	ECW H37/33R	Eastern National Omnibus Co	1541	RP
UHJ 842	1959	Bedford C4Z2	Duple C29F	Rochford Hospital (staff bus)		RP
SGD 407	1960	Leyland Titan PD3/2	Alexander H41/31F	Glasgow Corporation	L405	RP
373 WPU	1961	Guy Arab IV	Massey L34/33R	Moore Bros of Kelvedon		R
138 CLT	1962	AEC Routemaster R2RH	Park Royal H36/28R	London Transport	RM 1138	RP
28 TKR	1962	AEC Reliance 2MU3RV	Harrington C29F	Maidstone & District Motor Services	C28	R

Cobham Bus Museum

Contact address: Redhill Road, Cobham, Surrey, KT11 1EF
Phone/Fax: 01932 868665
Web site: www.lbpt.org.uk
E-mail: cobhambusmuseum@aol.com
Affiliation: NARTM
Brief description: This well-established museum was formed by a small group of enthusiasts in 1966. The collection has steadily grown over the years and now over 30 preserved buses are located at Cobham.
Events planned: Please see the enthusiast press for details.
Opening days/times: Open days as advertised.

Viewing possible at weekends 11.00 to 17.00 but please telephone in advance to confirm.
Directions by car: From M25 junction 10 take A3 north and turn left on to A245. Museum is 1 mile on left.
Directions by public transport: Museum bus service from Weybridge station on main events. Network of special services on annual open day.
Infrequent bus service at other times to Brooklands Road/Byfleet.
Charges: £2 but higher charges on open days.
Facilities: B B(e) G P R(limited) S T

Registration	Date	Chassis	Body	New to	Fleet No	Status
XX 9591	1925	Dennis 4-ton	Dodson O24/24RO	Dominion Omnibus Co		R
UU 6646	1929	AEC Regal 662	London General Omnibus Co B30R	London General Omnibus Co	T 31	R
GJ 2098	1930	AEC Regent 661	Thomas Tilling H27/25RO	Thomas Tilling	ST922	R
AXM 693	1934	AEC Regent 661	LPTB H30/26R	London Transport	STL 441	RP
LJ 9501	1934	Albion Valiant PV70	Harrington C32F	Charlies Cars of Bournemouth	57	RP
CGJ 188	1935	AEC Q 0762	Birmingham R C & W B35C	LPTB	Q 83	R
CXX 171	1936	AEC Regal 0662	Weymann C30F	LPTB	T 448	RP
DLU 92	1937	AEC Regent O661	LPTB H30/26R	LPTB	STL 2093	A
EGO 426	1938	AEC Regent O661	LPTB H30/26R	LPTB	STL 2377	R
ELP 228	1938	AEC Regal 0662	LPTB C30F	LPTB	T 504	R
HGC 130	1945	Guy Arab II	Park Royal UH30/26R	LPTB	G 351	RP
HLX 410	1948	AEC Regent III O961 RT	Weymann H30/26R	London Transport	RT 593	R
JXC 288	1949	Leyland Tiger PS1	Mann Egerton B30F	London Transport	TD 95	R
KGK 803	1949	Leyland Titan 7RT	Park Royal H30/26R	London Transport	RTL 139	R
MYA 590	1949	Leyland Comet CPO1	Harrington C29F	Scarlet Pimpernel of Minehead		R
UMP 227	1949	AEC Regal IV	Park Royal B40F	AEC prototype		A
LUC 210	1951	AEC Regal IV 9821LT RF	Metro Cammell DP35F	London Transport	RF 10	RP
LYR 826	1952	AEC Regent III O961 RT	Park Royal H30/26R	London Transport	RT 2775	RP
LYR 910	1952	AEC Regent III O961 RT	Park Royal H30/26R	London Transport	RT 3491	R
MLL 685	1952	Leyland Titan 7RT	Park Royal H30/26R	London Transport	RTL 1323	A
MLL 969	1952	AEC Regal IV 9821LT RF	Metro Cammell	London Transport	RF 332	R
NLE 534	1952	AEC Regal IV 9821LT RF	Metro Cammell B39F	London Transport	RF 534	R
MLL 740	1953	AEC Regal IV 9822E	Park Royal HDC37C	British European Airways		R
MXX 334	1953	Guy Special NLLVP	ECW B26F	London Transport	GS 34	R
NLE 672	1953	AEC Regal IV 9821LT RF	Metro Cammell B41F	London Transport	RF 672	R
CDX 516	1954	AEC Regent III 9613E	Park Royal H30/26R	Ipswich Corporation	16	R
SLT 58	1958	Leyland Routemaster	Weymann H34/30R	London Transport	RML 3	R
EGN 369J	1971	AEC Swift 4MP2R	Park Royal B33D	London Transport	SMS 369	R
JPA 190K	1972	AEC Reliance 6U2R	Park Royal DP45F	London Country Bus Services	RP 90	R
SPK 203M	1973	AEC Reliance 6U3ZR	Plaxton C49F	London Country Bus Services	P 3	R

Notes:

XX 9591	Restored as London General Omnibus Co D142	MYA 590	Converted from petrol to diesel in 1966
GJ 2098	On loan to BMMO during World War 2	JXC 288	Toured Europe and USSR 1963-1967
CXX 171	Used as an ambulance during World War 2	MLL 969	Converted to a towing vehicle in 1976
DLU 92	Original metal-framed Park Royal body replaced in 1949	LYR 910	Fitted with AEC 11.3 litre engine in 1998
ELP 228	Used as an ambulance during World War 2	LYR 826	Toured USA and Canada when new
HGC 130	Only remaining example of a London utility bus	SLT 58	Prototype Leyland Routemaster; renumbered RM3 in 1961
UMP 227	Prototype Regal IV - operated with London Transport in 1950		

Above: **Preservation pioneer London Transport AEC Regal T31 is a Cobham Bus Museum resident.**
Philip Lamb

Below: **Two more Cobham residents are Guy Special GS34 and AEC Q Q83.** *Philip Lamb*

Right: **Seen at Canterbury bus station is Dover Transport Museum's Park Royal-bodied AEC Reliance WFN 513, an East Kent dual-purpose vehicle.** *Philip Lamb*

Dover Transport Museum Whitfield

Contact address: Old Park, Whitfield, Dover, CT16 2HQ
Phone: 01304 822409/204612
Affiliation: NARTM, Transport Trust, AIM, ASTRO

Brief description: The museum displays local transport and social history. Road vehicles of all types. A maritime room, railway room, bygone shops and a garage. Hundreds of transport models including a working model tramway.

Events planned: Please see the enthusiast press for details.

Opening days/times: Easter to end June — Sundays 10.30 to 17.00; July, August and September — Thursdays and Fridays 14.00 to 17.00; Sundays 10.30 to 17.00.

Open at other times for pre-arranged groups.

Directions by car: Approximately one mile from the A2 Whitfield roundabout on the Dover bypass.

Directions by public transport: Dover Priory station then bus to Old Park, Whitfield.

Charges: Adult £2, Senior Citizen £1.50, Child £1, Family £5.

Facilities: B(e) D E G P R T

Registration	Date	Chassis	Body	New to	Fleet No	Status
CC 9305	1929	Dennis G	Roberts T19	Llandudno UDC		R
CJG 959	1947	Leyland Titan PD1A	Leyland L27/26R	East Kent Road Car Co		A
EFN 591	1950	Dennis Lancet J3	Park Royal C32F	East Kent Road Car Co		A
KXW 488	1950	AEC Regent III O961 RT	Weymann H30/26R	London Transport	RT 1389	RP
GFN 273	1952	Leyland Titan TD5	Beadle C35F	East Kent Road Car Co		R
MFN 898	1956	Guy Arab IV	Park Royal H33/28RD	East Kent Road Car Co		RP
569 KKK	1960	AEC Reliance 2MU3RA	Duple C41C	Ayers Coaches of Dover		R
WFN 513	1961	AEC Reliance 2MU3RV	Park Royal DP41F	East Kent Road Car Co		R
AFN 780B	1963	AEC Regent V 2D3RA	Park Royal H40/30F	East Kent Road Car Co		R
AFN 488B	1964	AEC Reliance 2MU4RA	Duple C34F	East Kent Road Car Co		RP
AFN 777B	1964	AEC Regent V 2D3RA	Park Royal H40/32F	East Kent Road Car Co		RP
GJG 751D	1966	AEC Regent V 2D3RA	Park Royal O40/32F	East Kent Road Car Co		R
OFN 721F	1968	AEC Reliance 6U3ZR	Marshall B53F	East Kent Road Car Co		RP
GFN 546N	1975	Leyland National 10351/1R	Leyland National B40F	East Kent Road Car Co	1546	RP

Notes:

EFN 591	Operated as a single-deck bus from June 1961
GFN 273	Rebuild of Leyland Titan TD5
GJG 751D	Originally H40/32F; used as promotional vehicle

Note: Please be aware that vehicles on display can vary from time to time as not all museums display their entire 'fleet'. Visitors wishing to see a particular vehicle should make enquiries prior to their visit.

Contact address: Chapel Road, Carlton Colville, Lowestoft, Suffolk, NR33 8BL
Phone: 01502 518459
Affiliation: NARTM & London Trolleybus Preservation Society.
Brief description: A working transport museum on a four-acre site, first opened in 1972 and run entirely by volunteers. Tram and trolleybus services operate regularly within a developing street scene and the tramway has a woodland section. There is also a narrow-gauge railway. A wide variety of other vehicles on display and sometimes operated includes buses, lorries, steam rollers, battery-electrics, tower wagons and a London taxi. The museum is a registered charity.

Events planned:
22/23 June 2002 — Steam & Bygones Spectacular
13/14 July 2002 — Bus Weekend 2002 — a tribute to Eastern Coach Works
10/11 August 2002 — Classic Vehicle Weekend
7/8 September 2002 — Trolleybus Weekend
Opening days/times: At Easter, then from May to September:
Sundays and Bank Holidays — 11.00 to 17.30;
Wednesdays and Saturdays (June to Sept) — 14.00 to 17.00;
All other days (late July and Aug) — 14.00 to 17.00.

Directions by car: Situated on the A1384. Follow the brown signs from the A12, A146 and A1117. New car park and entrance with access from Chapel Road, do not use the old hotel car park.
Directions by public transport:
Monday to Saturday: Eastern Counties bus L11 or L12 from Lowestoft bus station to Carlton Colville Church, then 8min walk or X71 and X74 to Carlton Colville and 5min walk.
Sundays and Bank Holidays: Eastern Counties bus L18 or L19 from Lowestoft bus station to the Museum.
New bus service 607 links Oulton Broad North and Oulton Broad South railway stations with the museum (Chapel Road bus stop), also links Great Yarmouth change at James Paget Hospital, for more details of this or other public transport information please ring the travel line on 08459 583358.
Every day X71 and X74 Lowestoft to Norwich, to Carlton Crown PH then 5min walk.
By train to Oulton Broad South then 35min walk or bus X71, X74 and 607.
Charges: £4.50 adults, £3 children/OAPs. Higher charges at special events. Admission includes free rides within the museum.
Facilities: B(e) D E F G H P R S T
Other information: Regular tram, train and trolleybus rides

Registration	Date	Chassis	Body	New to	Fleet No	Status
AH 79505+	1926	Garrett O type	Strachan & Brown B26D	NESA Copenhagen	5	RP
KW 1961	1927	Leyland Lion PLSC3	Leyland B35F	Blythe & Berwick of Bradford		A
ALJ 986+	1935	Sunbeam MS2	Park Royal O40/29R	Bournemouth Corporation	202	R
CUL 260+	1936	AEC 664T	Metro Cammell H40/30R	London Transport	260	R
EXV 201+	1938	Leyland LPTB70	Leyland H40/30R	London Transport	1201	R
FXH 521+	1940	Metro Cammell	Metro Cammell H40/30R	London Transport	1521	R
GBJ 192	1947	AEC Regent II O661	ECW H30/26R	Lowestoft Corporation	21	R
BDY 809+	1948	Sunbeam W	Weymann H30/26R	Hastings Tramways Co	34	RP
KAH 408	1948	Bristol L4G	ECW B35R	Eastern Counties Omnibus Co	LL 108	A
note d+	1948	Berna	Hess B37D	Biel (Switzerland)	39	R
LLU 829	1950	Leyland Titan 7RT	Park Royal H30/26R	London Transport	RTL 1050	R
NBB 628+	1950	BUT 9641T	Metro Cammell H40/30R	Newcastle Corporation	628	A
ERV 938+	1951	BUT 9611T	Burlingham H28/26R	Portsmouth Corporation	313	RP
SG 2030+	1952	Henschel uHIII/S	Uerdingen B32T	Solingen (Germany)	1	R
DRC 224+	1953	Sunbeam F4	Willowbrook H32/28R	Derby Corporation	224	R
LCD 52+	1953	BUT 9611T	Weymann H30/26R	Brighton Corporation	52	R
YTE 826+	1956	BUT 9612T	Bond H32/28R	Ashton under Lyne Corporation	87	R
2206 OI+	1958	Sunbeam F4A	Harkness H36/32R	Belfast Corporation	246	RP
YLJ 286+	1959	Sunbeam MF2B	Weymann H35/28D	Bournemouth Corporation	286	R
557 BNG	1962	Bristol Lodekka FL6G	ECW H37/33RD	Eastern Counties Omnibus Co	LFL 57	R
YRT 898H	1969	AEC Swift 2MP2R	ECW B45D	Lowestoft Corporation	4	R
OCK 985K	1972	Bristol VRTSL2/6LX	ECW H39/31F	Ribble Motor Services	1985	R

+ trolleybus

Notes:
AH 79505	Danish registration; being renovated in Copenhagen
ALJ 986	Converted to open top 1958
note d	Swiss Trolleybus; unregistered
SG 2030	German registration
LCD 52	Built 1950. First used 1953; Preserved in colours of subsequent operator Maidstone Corporation
2206 OI	Fitted with hydraulic brakes
OCK 985K	Acquired by Eastern Counties Omnibus Co (VR385) in 1985

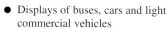

EATM is the home of many Trolleybuses, and houses a large collection of former London vehicles. Here is seen chassisless Metro-Cammell built LT No 1521, with wartime markings in use on the trolleybus circuit at Carlton Colville.
Paul Sampson

Grampian Transport Museum   Alford

Contact address: Alford, Aberdeenshire AB33 8AE
Phone: 01975 562292
Fax: 01975 562180
E-mail: info@g-t-m.freeserve.co.uk
Web site: www.gtm.org.uk
Brief description: Dramatic displays, working exhibits and video presentations trace the history of travel and transport.

Opening days/times: April to October inclusive, 10.00 to 17.00.
Directions by car: On A944 west from Aberdeen (27 miles).
Directions by public transport: Stagecoach bus services from Aberdeen.
Charges: £3.80 Adults, £3.10 Senior Citizens, £1.60 Children, £9.20.Family.
Facilities: A B(e) C D E FG H L M P R S T

Registration	Date	Chassis	Body	New to	Fleet No	Status
GAV 254	1950	Albion Victor FT3AB	Duple C31F	Spence, Alford		R
JFM 238D	1966	Bristol Lodekka FS6G	ECW H33/27RD	Crosville Motor Services	DFG238	R
NRG 154M	1974	Leyland Atlantean		Grampian Transport	154	R

Notes:
JFM 238D   Last rear entrance Bristol ever built
NRG 154M   Used as a video theatre

Imperial War Museum   London

Contact address: Lambeth Road, London SE1 6HZ
Phone:
020 7416 5320
0891 600140 (Recorded information)
E-mail: website: www.iwm.org.uk
Brief description: Revel in the history of the nation, through the world wars and much more besides. Regular exhibitions and displays of considerable educational value. The one bus in the collection fills a significant gap in transport history. Enquire before visiting on 020 7416 5211 to check bus is on display.
Opening days/times: Daily 10.00 to 18.00 (closed 24, 25 and 26 December)

Directions by car: South of Waterloo Station, close to the Elephant & Castle. Parking difficult but Coach Park at Vauxhall Bridge and disabled parking by prior arrangement only — phone 020 7416 5397.
Directions by public transport:
Underground to Lambeth North, Waterloo or Elephant & Castle. Rail to Waterloo.
Bus routes 1, 3, 12, 45, 53, 63, 68, 159, 168, 171, 172, 176, 188, 344 and C10.
Charges: Adult £5.20, Senior Citizen £4.20, Children free. Group rates available. Free after 16.30 daily.
Facilities: A C D G H R T

Registration	Date	Chassis	Body	New to	Fleet No	Status
LN 4743	1911	LGOC B	LGOC O18/16RO	London General Omnibus Co	B43	R

Note:
LN 4743   Named 'Ole Bill' after wartime cartoon character

Right: **Ipswich Transport Museum's latest restoration is ex-Eastern Counties Bristol L4G LL407.**
Mark Smith

Ipswich Transport Museum

Contact address: Old Trolleybus Depot, Cobham Road, Ipswich
IP3 9JD
Phone: 01473 715666
E-mail: www.ipswichtransportmuseum.co.uk.html
Affiliation: NARTM, ASTRO, TORA, SEMS, AFSM
Brief description: The collection includes most forms of road transport from the last 200 years, including bicycles, horse-drawn vehicles, trucks and service vehicles. There are displays of vehicles and other products of Ipswich engineering companies including six mobile cranes.
Events planned: Please see enthusiast press for details
Opening days/times: April to November: Sundays and Bank

Holidays 11.00 to 16.30
August and school half-term, Monday to Friday 13.00 to 16.00
Directions by car: From A12/A14 junction with A1189 (Nacton and Ipswich East) head towards Ipswich on Nacton Road. Turn right into Lindburgh Road. Museum is on left in Cobham Road.
Directions by public transport: By train to Ipswich. Take any bus to Town Centre.
Then take bus 2 to Cobham Road (Mon-Fri) or bus 75/76/77 (Suns) to Felixstowe Road railway bridge.
Charges: Adult £2.50, Child £1.50, Concessions £2, Family £7.
Facilities: A B(e) D G P R T, picnic area

Registration	Date	Chassis	Body	New to	Fleet No	Status
DX 3988+	1923	Railless	Short B30D	Ipswich Corporation	2	R
DX 5610+	1926	Ransomes Sims & Jefferies D	Ransomes Sims & Jefferies B31D	Ipswich Corporation	9	A
DX 5629+	1926	Garrett O type	Strachan & Brown B31D	Ipswich Corporation	26	A
note c+	1926	Ransomes Sims & Jefferies D	(chassis only)	Ipswich Corporation	16	R
DX 6591	1927	Tilling Stevens B9B	Eastern Counties B36R	Eastern Counties Road Car Co	78	A
VF 2788	1928	ADC 425A	Eastern Counties B36R	United Automobile Services	J379	A
DX 7812	1929	Tilling Stevens B10A2	(chassis only)	Eastern Counties Road Car Co	116	R
VF 8157	1930	Chevrolet LQ	Bush & Twiddy C140	Final of Hockwold		R
WV 1209	1932	Bedford WLB	Waveney B20F	Alexander of Devizes		A
PV 817+	1933	Ransomes Sims & Jefferies	Ransomes Sims & Jefferies H24/24R	Ipswich Corporation	46	A

Registration	Date	Chassis	Body	New to	Fleet No	Status
CVF 874	1939	Bristol L5G	ECW B35R	Eastern Counties Omnibus Co	LL 574	A
CAH 923	1940	Dennis Ace	ECW B20F	Eastern Counties Omnibus Co	D 23	RP
PV 8270+	1948	Karrier W	Park Royal H30/26R	Ipswich Corporation	105	A
KAH 407	1949	Bristol L4G	ECW B35R	Eastern Counties Omnibus Co	LL 407	R
KNG 374	1949	Bristol K6B	ECW L27/28R	Eastern Counties Omnibus Co	LK 374	A
PV 9371	1949	Bedford OB	Duple C27F	Mulleys Motorways of Ixworth		R
ADX 1	1950	AEC Regent III 9612E	Park Royal H30/26R	Ipswich Corporation	1	R
ADX 196+	1950	Sunbeam F4	Park Royal H30/26R	Ipswich Corporation	126	R
MAH 744	1951	Bristol LSX4G	ECW B42F	Eastern Counties Omnibus Co	LL 744	R
BPV 10	1953	AEC Regal IV 9822E	(chassis only)	Ipswich Corporation	10	A
BPV 9	1953	AEC Regal IV 9822E	Park Royal B42D	Ipswich Corporation	9	A
ADX 63B	1964	AEC Regent V 2D2RA	Massey H37/28R	Ipswich Corporation	63	R
APW 829B	1964	Bristol MW6G	ECW C39F	Eastern Counties Omnibus Co	LS 829	R
CNG 125C	1965	Bristol Lodekka FS5G	ECW H33/27RD	Eastern Counties Omnibus Co	LFS 125	RP
DPV 68D	1966	AEC Regent V 2D2RA	East Lancs Neepsend H37/28R	Ipswich Corporation	68	A
JRT 82K	1971	AEC Swift 2MP2R	Willowbrook B40D	Ipswich Corporation	82	R
MRT 6P	1976	Leyland Atlantean AN68/1R	Roe H43/29D	Ipswich Corporation	6	R
XNG 770S	1978	Leyland National 11351/1R	Leyland National B53F	Eastern Counties Omnibus Co	LN 770	A

+ Trolleybus

Notes:

DX 3988	Believed the oldest trolleybus on display in the world
DX 5610	Changed from solid to pneumatic tyres in 1930
note c	Chassis only
DX 6591	New with charabanc body; rebuilt in 1934
VF 2788	Original United body replaced in 1934
DX 7812	Rebodied twice while with Eastern Counties
PV 817	First Ipswich double decker
CVF 874	Originally numbered LL74
CAH 923	Originally fitted with Gardner 4LK engine
PV 8270	Originally fitted with wooden seats
KNG 374	Engine changed Gardner 5LW by Eastern Counties OC
ADX 1	Ipswich Corporation's first motor bus
MAH 744	Bristol LS prototype
VF 8157	Originally registered VF 9126; acquired by Mulleys Motorways of Ixworth in 1940

Isle of Wight Bus Museum — Newport (IoW)

Contact address: Seaclose Quay, Newport, Isle of Wight, PO30 2EF

Phone: 01983 533352

Affiliation: NARTM

Brief description: The collection ranges from a 1927 Daimler CK to a 1979 Ford R-series. Many of the vehicles are of Southern Vectis origin.

Events planned: 20 October 2002 — running day.

Opening days/times: 24 March-7 April: inclusive Tuesdays, Wednesdays, Thursdays and Sundays 10.00-16.00

2 June-29 September inclusive: Tuesdays, Wednesdays, Thursdays and Sundays 10.00-16.00

21 July -1 September: daily 10.30 to 16.00.

Directions by car: Access off Medina Way relief road and Sea Street. Left on to Quay. Bus museum is adjacent to Boat Museum (both signposted).

Directions by public transport: Bus to Newport bus station. Walk 12min to north of town.

Charges: £2 Adult, £1.50 Senior Citizen, £1 child.

Facilities: B(e) D G S

Other information: Car parking nearby. Refreshments and toilets at adjacent Boat Museum.

Registration	Date	Chassis	Body	New to	Fleet No	Status
DL 5084	1927	Daimler CK	Dodson B26R	Dodson Bros ('Vectis')	11	A
NG 1109	1931	Reo Pullman	Taylor Ch26D	Reynolds of Overstrand		
AUF 666§	1934	Leyland Titan TD3	Beadle H28/26R	Southdown Motor Services	966	RP

Below: **The Isle of Wight Bus Museum is home to this ex-Southern Vectis Bristol LD6G No 563.** *Philip Lamb*

Registration	Date	Chassis	Body	New to	Fleet No	Status
DL 9015§	1934	Dennis Ace	Harrington B20F	Southern Vectis Omnibus Co	405	RP
JT 8077	1937	Bedford WTB	Duple C25F	South Dorset Coaches		R
CAP 234	1940	Bristol K5G	ECW O30/26R	Brighton Hove & District	6350	RP
GDL 764	1950	Leyland PD2/1A	Leyland L53R	Seaview Services		
ODL 400	1957	Bedford SBG	Duple C41F	Moss Motor Tours of Sandown		RP
PDL 515§	1958	Bristol MW6G	ECW C39F	Southern Vectis Omnibus Co	315	RP
PDL 519	1958	Bristol Lodekka LD6G	ECW CO33/27R	Southern Vectis Omnibus Co	559	A
SDL 268	1959	Bristol Lodekka LD6G	ECW H33/27R	Southern Vectis Omnibus Co	563	R
CDL 479C	1965	Bristol Lodekka FLF6G	ECW H38/32F	Southern Vectis Omnibus Co	611	R
FDL 927D	1966	Bristol MW6G	ECW B43F	Southern Vectis Omnibus Co	806	R
KDL 885F	1968	Bristol RESH6G	Duple C45F	Southern Vectis Omnibus Co	301	R
VDL 264K	1972	Bedford YRQ	Plaxton Derwent B49F	Seaview Services		
MDL 880R§	1976	Leyland National 11351A/1R	Leyland National B52F	Southern Vectis Omnibus Co	880	A
YDL 135T	1979	Ford R1014	Duple B47F	Isle of Wight County Council	5809	A

§Reserve collection

Notes:

AUF 666	Rebodied 1949
CAP 234	Originally H30/26R Converted to open top 1952. To Southern Vectis in 1960.
PDL 519	Originally H33/27R
CDL 479C	Owned by Southern Vectis and loaned to museum
FDL 927D	Owned by Southern Vectis and loaned to museum
KDL 885F	Owned by Southern Vectis and loaned to museum

In 1966, Leeds 131, a Roe-bodied Daimler Fleetline was a Commercial Motor Show exhibit. Today it is on show at Keighley Bus Museum. *Philip Lamb*

Keighley Bus Museum

Keighley & Denholme

Contact address: 47 Brantfell Drive, Burnley, Lancs BB12 8AW
Phone: 01282 413179
Affiliation: NARTM
Brief description: A collection of buses, coaches and ancillary vehicles. Some are owned by the Trust and others by private individuals. The Trust aims to establish a permanent home for the collection in central Keighley.
Events planned: Please see the enthusiast press for details.
Opening days/times: Currently under review, please enquire for details.

The Museum is located on two sites: Old Dalton Lane (Keighley) adjacent to railway station and at Denholme behind the Parish Church.
Directions by car: Between Keighley and Halifax, at Denholme.
Directions by public transport: Keighley (adjacent to main line station) and 5min from bus station. Frequent buses from Keighley and Bradford to Denholme.
Charges: Special events: £2 Adult, £1 concession. Otherwise free but donations welcome.
Facilities: B(e) P T

Registration	Date	Chassis	Body	New to	Fleet No	Status
WT 7101+	1924	Straker Clough	Brush H50R	Keighley Corporation Tramways	5	R
KW 2260	1927	Leyland Lion PLSC3	Leyland B35R	Bradford Corporation	325	A
TF 6860	1931	Leyland Lion LT3	Leyland B36R	Rawtenstall Corporation	61	RP
ANW 682	1934	AEC Regent 661	Roe H30/26R	Leeds City Transport	139	R
DKT 11	1937	Leyland Tiger TS7	Harrington C32R	Maidstone & District Motor Services	CO553	A
CFM 354	1938	Leyland Titan TD5	ECW L26/26R	Crosville Motor Services	M52	RP
CWX 671	1938	Bristol K5G	Roe L27/28R	Keighley-West Yorkshire Services	KDG 26	R
EUF 198	1938	Leyland Titan TD5	Short -	Southdown Motor Services	0198	R
RN 8622	1939	Leyland Titan TD5	Alexander L27/26R	Ribble Motor Services	2057	R
CUH 856	1947	Leyland Tiger PS1	ECW B35R	Western Welsh Omnibus Co	856	A
FWW 596	1947	Bedford OB	Duple C26F	West Yorkshire Road Car Co	646	A
FWX 914+	1948	Sunbeam F4	East Lancs H37/29F	Bradford Corporation	844	R
HOD 30	1948	Bristol L6A	Beadle C31F	Western National Omnibus Co (Royal Blue)	1228	R
MNW 86	1948	Leyland Tiger PS1	Roe B36R	Leeds City Transport	28	R
EVD 406	1949	Crossley DD42/7	Roe H31/25R	Baxter's Bus Service of Airdrie	34	R
NNW 492	1949	AEC Regent III 9612E	Roe H31/25R	Leeds City Transport	492	RP
NUB 609	1950	AEC Regent III 9612E	(chassis only)	Leeds City Transport	609	A
JWU 886	1951	Bristol LL5G	ECW B39R	West Yorkshire Road Car Co	SGL16	R
LYR 533	1951	AEC Regent III O961 RT	Park Royal H30/26R	London Transport	RT 3314	R
NHN 128	1951	Bristol LL6B	ECW DP33R	United Automobile Services	BBE1	
HKW 82	1952	AEC Regent III 9613E	East Lancs H31/28R	Bradford Corporation	82	R
PJX 43	1952	Leyland Titan PD2/37	Weymann H36/28F	Halifax Corporation	43	RP
AEK 514	1953	Leyland Royal Tiger PSU1/13	Northern Counties B44F	Wigan Corporation	101	A
LWR 424	1953	Bristol KSW6G	ECW	West Yorkshire Road Car Co	4044	R
SVS 904	1954	Bristol LS6G	ECW C35F	Southern National Omnibus Co	1381	R
JVH 381	1955	AEC Regent III 9613E	East Lancs H35/28R	Huddersfield Corporation	181	A
PGK 872	1955	Bedford SBG	Mulliner B30F	Ministry of Supply		A
UUA 214	1955	Leyland Titan PD2/11	Roe H33/25R	Leeds City Transport	214	RP
GJX 331	1956	Daimler CVG6	Roe H37/26R	Halifax Corporation	119	R
VTU 76	1956	Daimler CVG6	Northern Counties H35/23C	SHMD Board	76	R
XLG 477	1956	Atkinson Alpha PL745H	Northern Counties B34C	SHMD Board	77	A
KAG 856	1957	Leyland Titan PD2/20	Alexander L31/28R	Western SMT Co	1375	RP
SYG 561	1957	Bedford SBG	Duple C41F	Walton & Helliwell of Mytholmroyd		A
DHD 177	1959	AEC Regent V 2LD3RA	MCW H39/31F	Yorkshire Woollen District Transport Co	797	A
PJX 232	1962	Leyland Leopard L1	Weymann B44F	Halifax Joint Omnibus Committee	232	R
WBR 246	1963	Atkinson Alpha PM746HL	Marshall B45D	Sunderland Corporation	46	RP
6220 KW	1964	AEC Regent V 2D3RA	MCW H40/30F	Bradford Corporation	220	R
TRN 731	1964	Leyland Leopard PSU3/3R	Plaxton C49F	Ribble Motor Services	7315	R
ENW 980D	1966	AEC Regent V 2D2RA	Roe H39/31R	Leeds City Transport	980	RP
HNW 131D	1966	Daimler Fleetline CRG6LX	Roe H45/33F	Leeds City Transport	131	R
KVH 473E	1966	Daimler Fleetline CRG6LX	Roe H44/31F	Huddersfield Corporation	473	R
KWT 642D	1966	Bristol Lodekka FS6B	ECW H33/27RD	West Yorkshire Road Car Co	DX210	R
NWU 265D	1966	Bristol Lodekka FS6B	ECW H33/27RD	York - West Yorkshire Joint Committee	YDX221	A

Registration	Date	Chassis	Body	New to	Fleet No	Status
TWW 766F	1967	Bristol RELH6G	ECW C47F	West Yorkshire Road Car Co	CRG6	R
YLG 717F	1967	Bristol RESL6G	Northern Counties B43F	SHMD Board	117	A
BWU 691H	1969	Leyland Leopard PSU4A/2R	Pennine B43F	Todmorden Joint Omnibus Committee	19	A
LAK 309G	1969	Leyland Titan PD3A/12	Alexander H41/29F	Bradford Corporation	309	R
LAK 313G	1969	Leyland Titan PD3A/12	Alexander H41/29F	Bradford Corporation	313	A
WFM 801K	1972	Leyland National 1151/2R/0403	Leyland National B44D	Crosville Motor Services	SNL801	R
XAK 355L	1972	Daimler Fleetline CRL6	Alexander H43/31F	Bradford Corporation	355	RP
OWT 776M	1974	Bristol RELL6G	ECW B53F	West Yorkshire Road Car Co	1403	R
MUA 45P	1976	Bristol LHS6L	ECW DP27F	West Yorkshire PTE	45	A
MUA 870P	1976	Leyland Atlantean AN68/1R	Roe H43/30F	Yorkshire Woollen District Transport Co	773	R
PUM 149W +Trolleybus	1980	Bristol VRTSL3/6LXB	ECW H43/31F	West Yorkshire Road Car Co	1746	A

Notes:

WT 7101	Solid tyres
TF 6860	Used as a tow bus and snow plough 1950-1963
CWX 671	Rebodied 1950
EUF 198	Converted to a towing vehicle from bus 198 in 1957
RN 8622	Chassis refurbished and rebodied in 1949
FWX 914	Rebodied 1963
NNW 492	Leeds City Transport driver trainer 1968-71
EVD 406	New with Scottish Commercial body; acquired by J Wood & Son of Mirfield in 1953 and rebodied 1955
JWU 886	Single block experimental Gardner engine
LWR 424	Originally bus 858 (later DGW4); converted to a towing vehicle and renumbered 4044 in 1972
SVS 904	Originally registered OTT 90
UUA 214	Leeds City Transport driver trainer 1972-78
KWT 642D	Renumbered 1810 in 1971
NWU 265D	Renumbered 3821 in 1971
TWW 766F	Renumbered 1019 in 1971; restored in later guise as 2508
WFM 801K	Second production Leyland National delivered as B44D; converted to single door by Greater Manchester Buses (South)
OWT 776M	Delivered with Leyland O680 engine

Above left: **Former Halifax Daimler CVG6/Roe 119 is one of a number of former Transperience exhibits now at Keighley Bus Museum.** *Philip Lamb*

Left: **Roe-bodied Daimler Fleetline Huddersfield 473 has also made the journey from Transperience to Keighley.** *Philip Lamb*

Note: Please be aware that vehicles on display can vary from time to time as not all museums display their entire 'fleet'. Visitors wishing to see a particular vehicle should make enquiries prior to their visit.

Lincolnshire Road Transport Museum   North Hykeham

Contact address: Whisby Road, North Hykeham, Lincoln LN6 3QT
Phone: 01522 689497
Web site: www.lvvs.freeserve.co.uk
Affiliation: NARTM
Brief description: An impressive collection of over 50 vehicles including classic cars, commercials, buses and motor cycles, mostly with Lincolnshire connections. Sixty years of road transport history is represented in the museum hall, which was built in 1993. An extension to the hall is planned.
Events planned: Open day on 3 Nov 2002
Opening days/times:
May to October: Monday to Friday 12.00 to 16.00; Sunday 10.00 to 16.00;

November to April: Sunday 12.00 to 17.00. Other times by appointment.
Directions by car: Just off A46 Lincoln by-pass on Whisby Road, which links A46 to B1190.
Directions by public transport:
1 mile from North Hykeham railway station.
Whisby Road is just off Doddington Road, served by several bus routes from city centre.
Charges: No charge but donations welcome.
Facilities: A B(e) D P T
Other information: Refreshments available on open days.

Registration	Date	Chassis	Body	New to	Fleet No	Status
KW 474	1927	Leyland Lion PLSC1	Leyland B31F	Blythe & Berwick of Bradford		R
TE 8318	1929	Chevrolet LQ	Spicer C14D	Jardine of Morcambe		R
VL 1263	1929	Leyland Lion LT1	Applewhite B32R	Lincoln Corporation	5	R
WH 1553	1929	Leyland Titan TD1	Leyland L27/24RO	Bolton Corporation	54	R
KW 7604	1930	Leyland Badger TA4	Plaxton B20F	Bradford Education Committee	023	R
TF 818	1930	Leyland Lion LT1	Roe B30F	Lancashire United Transport	202	R
FW 5698	1935	Leyland Tiger TS7	Burlingham B35F	Lincolnshire Road Car Co	1411	R
RC 2721	1935	SOS DON	Brush B—F	Trent Motor Traction Co	321	R
FHN 833	1940	Bristol L5G	ECW B35F	United Automobile Services	BLO133	RP
BFE 419	1941	Leyland Titan TD7	Roe H30/26R	Lincoln Corporation	64	R
AHE 163	1946	Leyland Titan PD1	Roe H31/25R	Yorkshire Traction	726	RP
DBE 187	1946	Bristol K6A	ECW H30/26R	Lincolnshire Road Car Co	2115	RP
DFE 383	1948	Guy Arab III	Guy H30/26R	Lincoln Corporation	23	R
HPW 133	1949	Bristol K5G	ECW H30/26R	Eastern Counties Omnibus Co	LKH 133	R
OHK 432	1949	Daimler CVD6	Roberts H30/26R	Colchester Corporation	4	R
ONO 59	1949	Bristol K5G	ECW	Eastern National Omnibus Co	4038	R
FFU 860	1950	AEC Regal III 9621E	Willowbrook DP35F	Enterprise of Scunthorpe	60	R
LTB 907	1950	Bedford OB	Duple C29F	Penn of Warrington		R
FDO 573	1953	AEC Regent III 9613E	Willowbrook H32/28RD	J W Camplin & Sons ('Holme Delight') of Donington		RP
OLD 714	1954	AEC Regent III O961 RT	Weymann H30/26R	London Transport	RT 4494	R
LFW 326	1955	Bristol Lodekka LD6B	ECW H33/25RD	Lincolnshire Road Car Co	2318	R
RFE 416	1961	Leyland Titan PD2/41	Roe H33/28R	Lincoln Corporation	89	R
952 JUB	1964	AEC Regent V 2D2RA	Roe H39/31R	Leeds City Transport	952	RP
EVL 549E	1967	Leyland Panther PSUR1/1R	Roe DP45F	Lincoln Corporation	41	RP
UVL 873M	1973	Bristol RELL6L	Alexander B48F	Lincoln Corporation	73	RP
PFE 542V	1980	Bristol VRT	ECW H74F	Lincolnshire Road Car Co	1958	RP

Notes:

KW 474	Restored as Lincoln Corporation No 1
FW 5698	Rebodied 1949
DFE 383	Ruston Hornsby air cooled engine
ONO 59	Renumbered 1427 in 1954 and 2255 in 1964; subsequently converted to caravan
FFU 860	Passed to Lincolnshire Road Car Co (860) in 1950

London's Transport Museum   Covent Garden

Contact address: 39 Wellington Street, London WC2E 7BB.
Phone: 020 7379 6344; recorded information 020 7565 7299
E-mail: resources@ltmuseum.co.uk
Web site: www.ltmuseum.co.uk
Affiliation: NARTM
Brief description: Visit London's Transport Museum and see how public transport has transformed the capital and lives of Londoners since the early 1800s. It's trams, trains, buses and much more. A truly memorable hands-on experience.
Opening days/times: Daily 10.00 to 18.00 (Fri 11.00 to 18.00) Last admission 17.15. Closed 24, 25 and 26 December.

Directions by car: Limited parking at parking meters in Covent Garden, Holborn/Kingsway area.
Directions by public transport:
Buses to Strand or Aldwych: 1, 4, 6, 9, 11, 13, 15, 23, 26, 59, 68, 76, 77A, 91, 168, 171, 172, 176, 188, 243 and 341
Underground to Covent Garden, Leicester Square or Holborn.
Charges: Adult £5.95, Concession £4.50, Accompanied children under 16s free, other prices available — contact the Museum for details. For school rates please telephone Resource Centre.
Facilities: A C D F G H L R S T

Registration	Date	Chassis	Body	New to	Fleet No	Status
note m	1829	Horse bus	LGOC	George Shillibeer		R
note n	1875	Horse bus	Thomas Tilling -24-	Thomas Tilling		R
note p	1888	Horse bus	LGOC -26-	London General Omnibus Co		R
LC 3701	1906	De Dion	(chassis only)	London General Omnibus Co	L7	R
LA 9928	1911	LGOC B	LGOC O18/16RO	London General Omnibus Co	B340	R
XC 8059	1921	AEC K	LGOC O24/22RO	London General Omnibus Co	K424	R
MN 2615	1923	Tilling Stevens TS3A Petrol Electric	(chassis only)	Douglas Corporation	10	R
XM 7399	1923	AEC S	LGOC O28/26RO	London General Omnibus Co	S742	R
YR 3844	1926	AEC NS	LGOC H28/24RO	London General Omnibus Co	NS1995	R
GK 3192	1931	AEC Regent 661	LGOC H28/20R	London General Omnibus Co	ST821	R
GK 5323	1931	AEC Renown 663	LGOC H33/23R	London General Omnibus Co	LT165	R
GK 5486	1931	AEC Regal 662	Duple C30F	London General Omnibus Co	T219	R
GO 5198	1931	AEC Renown 664	LGOC B—F	London General Omnibus Co	LT1076	RP
HX 2756+	1931	AEC 663T	UCC H32/24R	London United Tramways	1	R
AXM 649	1934	AEC Regent 661	Chalmers -	London Transport		R
AYV 651	1934	AEC Regent 661	LPTB H30/26R	London Transport	STL469	R
BXD 576	1935	AEC Q 0762	Birmingham R C & W B35C	London Transport	Q55	R
CLE 122	1936	Leyland Cub KP03	Weymann B20F	London Transport	C94	R
EXV 253+	1939	Leyland LPTB70	Leyland H40/30R	London Transport	1253	R
FJJ 774	1939	Leyland FEC	LPTB B34F	London Transport	TF77	R
HYM 768+	1948	BUT 9641T	Metro Cammell H40/30R	London Transport	1768	R
MXX 364	1953	Guy Special NLLVP	ECW B26F	London Transport	GS64	R
NLE 537	1953	AEC Regal IV 9821LT RF	Metro Cammell B39F	London Transport	RF537	R
NXP 997	1954	AEC Regent III O961 RT	Park Royal H30/26R	London Transport	RT4712	R
OLD 589	1954	AEC Regent III O961 RT	Park Royal H30/26R	London Transport	RT4825	R
SLT 56	1956	AEC Routemaster	Park Royal/LTE H36/28R	London Transport	RM1	R
SLT 57	1957	AEC Routemaster	Park Royal/LTE H36/28R	London Transport	RM2	R
737 DYE	1963	AEC Routemaster 2R2RH	Park Royal H36/28R	London Transport	RM1737	R
CUV 229C	1965	AEC Routemaster R2RH/1	Park Royal H36/29RD	London Transport	RCL2229	R
KGY 4D	1966	AEC Routemaster FR2R	Park Royal H41/31F	London Transport	FRM1	RP
AML 582H	1969	AEC Merlin 4P2R	MCW B25D	London Transport	MBA582	R
EGP 1J	1970	Daimler Fleetline CRG6LXB	Park Royal H44/24D	London Transport	DMS1	R
KJD 401P	1976	Bristol LH6L	ECW B39F	London Transport	BL1	A
NUW 567Y	1982	Leyland Titan TNLXB/2RR	Leyland H44/24D	London Transport	T567	R
C526 DYT	1986	Volkswagen LT55	Optare B25F	London Transport	OV2	R
note r	1993	Optare Metrorider	Optare B26F	London Transport	MRL242	R
+ Trolleybus						

Notes:

note m	Unregistered reconstruction	SLT 56	New 9/1954. First Registered 1/1956.
note n	Unregistered	SLT 57	New 1955. First Registered 5/1957.
note p	Unregistered; Garden Seat type	note r	Unregistered sectioned exhibit built especially for
AXM 649	Rebuilt with Breakdown Vehicle body in 1950		LT Museum

Manchester Museum of Transport — Cheetham

Contact address: Boyle Street, Cheetham, Manchester M8 8UL
Phone/Fax: 0161 205 2122
E-mail: gmts.enquire@btinternet.com
Web site: www.gmts.co.uk
Affiliation: NARTM
Brief description:
The museum houses over 70 buses and coaches from the Greater Manchester area, from an 1876 horse bus to a 1990 Metrolink tram. Travel back to a time of twopenny singles and coach trips to Blackpool. Extensive displays of photos, uniforms and models complement the vehicles, and visitors may enter many of the vehicles and view the museum's workshop.
Events planned:
11/12 May 2002 — 100 Years of Transport in Salford
15/16 June 2002 — Accessible Transport Weekend
27/28 July 2002 — Festival of Model Tramways
1 September 2002 — Trans-Lancs Rally
30 November/1 December 2002 — Christmas Cracker Festival
Opening days/times: Wednesdays, Saturdays, Sundays & Bank Holidays: 10.00 to 17.00 (please phone for Christmas/New Year opening)
Directions by car:
From M62/M60 junction 18, follow 'Castlefields' signs to Cheetham Hill; from City, follow A665 (Cheetham Hill Road) — Museum signposted.
Directions by public transport:
Bus 135 or 59 to Queen's Road; Metrolink tram to Woodlands Road (10min walk)
Charges: £3.00 adult, £1.75 concession, £9 family. Season tickets available. School parties free
Facilities: B(e) C D F G H P R S T
Other information: Archives available for study by arrangement.

Registration	Date	Chassis	Body	New to	Fleet No	Status
note b	1876	Horse bus	Manchester Carriage Co O18/14RO	Manchester Carriage Co	2	R
DB 5070	1925	Tilling Stevens TS6	Brush O54RO	North Western Road Car Co	170	R
CK 3825	1927	Leyland Lion PLSC1	Leyland B31F	Ribble Motor Services	295	R
VM 4439	1928	Leyland Tiger TS1	Metro Cammell/Crossley B32R	Manchester Corporation	138	A
VY 957	1929	Leyland Lion PLSC1	Ribble B32R	York Corporation	2	R
VR 5742	1930	Leyland Tiger TS2	Manchester Corporation Car Works B30R	Manchester Corporation	28	R
AXJ 857	1934	Leyland Titan TD3	(chassis only)	Manchester Corporation	526	R
JA 7585	1935	Leyland Tiger TS7	English Electric B35C	Stockport Corporation	185	A
RN 7824	1936	Leyland Cheetah LZ2	Brush C31F	Ribble Motor Services	1568	RP
EFJ 92	1938	Bedford WTB	Heaver C25F	Taylor of Exeter		RP
AJA 152	1939	Bristol K5G	Willowbrook L27/26R	North Western Road Car Co	432	R
BBA 560	1939	AEC Regent O661	Park Royal H26/22R	Salford Corporation	235	R
JP 4712	1940	Leyland Titan TD7	Leyland L27/26R	Wigan Corporation	70	RP
BJA 425	1946	Bristol L5G	Willowbrook B38R	North Western Road Car Co	270	R
HTB 656	1946	Leyland Tiger PS1	Roe B35R	Ramsbottom Corporation	17	R
HTF 586	1947	Bedford OB	Scottish Motor Traction C29F	Warburton Bros of Bury		R
CDB 224	1948	Leyland Titan PD2/1	Leyland L27/26R	North Western Road Car Co	224	R
CWH 717	1948	Leyland Titan PD2/4	Leyland	Bolton Corporation	367	R
JND 791	1948	Crossley DD42/8S	Crossley H32/26R	Manchester Corporation	2150	R
JNA 467	1949	Leyland Titan PD1/3	Metro Cammell H32/26R	Manchester Corporation	3166	RP
LMA 284	1949	Foden PVSC6	Lawton C35F	Coppenhall of Comberbach		R
BEN 177	1950	AEC Regent III 9613A	Weymann H30/26R	Bury Corporation	177	R
CWG 206	1950	Leyland Tiger PS1	Alexander C35F	W Alexander & Sons	PA164	R
LTC 774+	1950	Crossley Empire TDD42/2	Crossley H30/26R	Ashton-under-Lyne Corporation	80	RP
MTB 848	1950	Leyland Tiger PS2/1	East Lancs B35R	Rawtenstall Corporation	55	RP
EDB 549	1951	Leyland Titan PD2/1	Leyland O30/20R	Stockport Corporation	295	R
EDB 562	1951	Leyland Titan PD2/1	Leyland H30/26R	Stockport Corporation	308	R
EDB 575	1951	Crossley DD42/7	Crossley H30/26R	Stockport Corporation	321	R
HDK 835	1951	AEC Regent III 9612E	East Lancs H31/26R	Rochdale Corporation	235	RP
JND 646	1951	Leyland Titan PD2/3	Metro Cammell H32/26R	Manchester Corporation	3245	R
JVU 775+	1951	Crossley Dominion TDD64/1	Crossley H36/30R	Manchester Corporation	1250	R

Above right: **In total four Leyland Panther Cubs survive. With Park Royal body, Manchester 74 is now back on the road after a brief absence.** *Philip Lamb*

Right: **Manchester Leyland PD2s Nos 3460 and 3520 display contrasting bodystyles by Metro-Cammell and Burlingham respectively.** *Philip Lamb*

Registration	Date	Chassis	Body	New to	Fleet No	Status
NNB 125	1953	Leyland Royal Tiger PSU1/13	Northern Counties B41C	Manchester Corporation	25	R
UTC 672	1954	AEC Regent III 9613S	East Lancs L27/28RD	Bamber Bridge Motor Services	4	R
UMA 370	1955	Atkinson PD746	Northern Counties H35/24C	SHMD Board	70	R
JBN 153	1956	Leyland Titan PD2/13	Metro Cammell H34/28R	Bolton Corporation	77	R
NDK 980	1956	AEC Regent V D2RA6G	Weymann H33/28R	Rochdale Corporation	280	R
PND 460	1956	Leyland Titan PD2/12	Metro Cammell H36/28R	Manchester Corporation	3460	R
DJP 754	1957	Leyland Titan PD2/30	Northern Counties H33/28R	Wigan Corporation	115	R
NBU 494	1957	Leyland Titan PD2/20	Roe H31/29R	Oldham Corporation	394	R
116 JTD	1958	Guy Arab IV	Northern Counties H41/32R	Lancashire United Transport	21	R
122 JTD	1958	Guy Arab IV	Northern Counties H41/32R	Lancashire United Transport	27	R
TNA 496	1958	Leyland Titan PD2/40	Burlingham H37/28R	Manchester Corporation	3496	R
TNA 520	1958	Leyland Titan PD2/34	Burlingham H37/28R	Manchester Corporation	3520	R
YDK 590	1960	AEC Reliance 2MU3RA	Harrington C37F	Yelloway Motor Services of Rochdale		R
HEK 705	1961	Leyland Titan PD3A/2	Massey H41/29F	Wigan Corporation	57	R
TRJ 112	1962	Daimler CVG6	Metro Cammell H37/28R	Salford City Transport	112	R
414 CLT	1963	AEC Routemaster 2R2RH	Park Royal H36/28R	London Transport	RM 1414	R
4632 VM	1963	Daimler CVG6K	Metro Cammell H37/28R	Manchester Corporation	4632	R
REN 116	1963	Leyland Atlantean PDR1/1	Metro Cammell H41/33F	Bury Corporation	116	R
8860 VR	1964	AEC Regent V 2D3RA	East Lancs Neepsend H41/32R	A Mayne & Son of Manchester		R
BND 874C	1965	Leyland Panther Cub PSURC1/1	Park Royal B43D	Manchester Corporation	74	R
DBA 214C	1965	Leyland Atlantean PDR1/1	Metro Cammell H43/33F	Salford City Transport	214	R
DDB 174C	1965	Daimler Fleetline CRG6LX	Alexander H44/31F	North Western Road Car Co	174	R
PTC 114C	1965	AEC Renown 3B3RA	East Lancs H41/31F	Leigh Corporation	15	R
PTE 944C	1965	Leyland Titan PD2/37	Roe H37/28F	Ashton-under-Lyne Corporation	44	R
FRJ 254D	1966	Leyland Titan PD2/40	Metro Cammell H36/28F	Salford City Transport	254	R
JRJ 281E	1967	Leyland Titan PD2/40	Metro Cammell H36/28F	Salford City Transport	281	R
HVM 901F	1968	Leyland Atlantean PDR1/1	Park Royal H45/28D	Manchester City Transport	1001	R
KDB 408F	1968	Leyland Leopard PSU4/1R	East Lancs B43D	Stockport Corporation	408	RP
KJA 871F	1968	Leyland Titan PD3/14	East Lancs H38/32R	Stockport Corporation	71	R
MJA 891G	1969	Leyland Titan PD3/14	East Lancs H38/32R	Stockport Corporation	91	R
MJA 897G	1969	Leyland Titan PD3/14	East Lancs O38/32F	Stockport Corporation	97	R
TTD 386H	1969	Leyland Titan PD3/14	East Lancs H41/32F	Ramsbottom Corporation	11	R
TXJ 507K	1972	Leyland National 1151/2R/0202	Leyland National B46D	SELNEC PTE	EX30	R
VNB 101L	1972	Leyland Atlantean AN68/1R	Park Royal H43/32F	SELNEC PTE	7001	R
XVU 352M	1974	Seddon Pennine IV-236	Seddon B19F	SELNEC PTE	1722	A
GNC 276N	1975	Seddon Lucas	Seddon B19F	Greater Manchester PTE	EX62	R
HVU 244N	1975	AEC Reliance 6U3ZR	Plaxton C49F	Yelloway Motor Services of Rochdale		R
ORJ 83W	1981	MCW Metrobus DR102/21	MCW H43/30F	Greater Manchester PTE	5083	A
A706 LNC	1984	Leyland Atlantean AN68D/1R	Northern Counties H43/32F	Greater Manchester PTE	8706	A
D63 NOF	1986	Freight Rover 400 Special	Carlyle B18F	Manchester Minibuses (Bee Line Buzz Co.)		A

+ Trolleybus

Notes:

note b	Largest surviving horse bus.	EDB 549	Originally H30/26R
DB 5070	Petrol Electric transmission	UMA 370	Only Atkinson double-decker bodied. Originally H35/25C.
CK 3825	Body rebuilt 1981	414 CLT	Loaned to Manchester Corporation when new in Feb 1963
VM 4439	Body new 1935	HVM 901F	First 'Mancunian' double-decker
VY 957	Body rebuilt 1983; restored to Ribble livery	TTD 386H	Last half-cab double-decker delivered to a British operator
VR 5742	Rebodied 1937	MJA 897G	Originally H38/32F; converted to open-top in 1982
AJA 152	Rebodied 1951	MJA 891G	Last open-rear-platform double-decker delivered to a British operator
BJA 425	Originally numbered 125; rebodied 1958 with 1952 body		
CWH 717	Originally H30/26R; converted to tower wagon 1963.	VNB 101L	First SELNEC Standard double-decker
LMA 284	Body new 1954	TXJ 507K	First production Leyland National
EDB 562	Used as training bus 1968-1978	GNC 276N	Battery-powered

Museum of British Road Transport   Coventry

Contact address: Hales Street, Coventry CV1 1PN
Phone: 024 7683 2425
Fax: 024 7683 2465
E-mail: museum@mbrt.co.uk
Brief description: The museum has over 210 cars and commercial vehicles, over 90 motorcycles and around 240 bicycles. Various tableaux chart the development of the motor vehicle from the early years, and Coventry's contribution to this can be seen in the many marques on display. Other exhibits include a 633mph land speed record car, several thousand die-cast models and a walk through audio visual display of the Coventry Blitz experience.

Events planned: Please see the enthusiast press for details.
Opening days/times: Seven days a week, 10.00 to 17.00 (except Christmas Eve, Christmas Day and Boxing Day.)
Directions by car: Follow brown 'Motor Museum' signs from Coventry City Centre.
Directions by public transport: Museum is close to Pool Meadow bus station; use bus 17 or 27 from Coventry railway station to Pool Meadow.
Charges: Free admission
Facilities: A D F G H L R S T

Registration	Date	Chassis	Body	New to	Fleet No	Status
Note t	1916	Maudslay	no body			A
EKV 966	1944	Daimler CWA6	Roe H31/25R	Coventry Corporation	366	R
JNB 416	1948	Maudslay Marathon II	Trans-United C33F	Hackett's of Manchester		R
KOM 150	1950	Daimler CVD6	Wilsdon -	Birmingham Post & Mail		R
SRB 424	1953	Daimler CD650	Willowbrook L27/28RD	Tailby & George ('Blue Bus Services') Willington		R
PBC 734	1954	Karrier Bantam Q25	Reading C14F	Mablethorpe Homes of Leicester		R
333 CRW	1963	Daimler CVG6	Metro Cammell H34/29R	Coventry Corporation	333	R
PDU 125M	1973	Daimler Fleetline CRG6LX	East Lancs O44/30F	Coventry Corporation	125	R

Notes:

Note t	To be restored as replica of 1921 Hickman bodied bus for Coventry Corporation
EKV 966	Rebodied 1951; converted to mobile repair workshop (O2) in 1960
KOM 150	Currently used as museum promotional vehicle
PBC 734	Welfare bus
PDU 125M	Originally H44/30F; converted to open top in 1986

Many Maudslay Marathon IIIs were bodied by lesser bodybuilders. That carried by the Museum of British Road Transport's JNB 416 was by Trans-United. *Museum of British Road Transport, Coventry*

Museum of Transport   Glasgow

Contact address: Kelvin Hall, 1 Bunhouse Road, Glasgow G3 8DP
Phone: 0141 287 2720 (school bookings on 0141 287 2747)
Fax: 0141 287 2692
Affiliation: NARTM
Brief description: The museum displays many items of transport history dating from the 1870s.
Opening days/times: Monday to Saturday, 10.00 to 17.00; Sunday 11.00 to 17.00 (closed 25/26 December and 1/2 January)

Directions by car: From M8 junctions 17 or 19
Directions by public transport: Bus from City Centre (Dumbarton Road) to Kelvin Hall; Underground to Kelvin Hall; nearest main-line railway station is Partick.
Charges: Free admission
Facilities: D F G H R T
Other information: Guided tours and exhibitions also held.

Registration	Date	Chassis	Body	New to	Fleet No	Status
EGA 79	1949	Albion Venturer CX 37S	Croft H30/26R	Glasgow Corporation	B92	R
FYS 988+	1958	BUT RETB1	Burlingham B50F	Glasgow Corporation	TBS13	R
FYS 998	1958	Leyland Atlantean PDR1/1	Alexander H44/34F	Glasgow Corporation	LA1	R
+Trolleybus						

Notes:
FYS 988   Exhibited at the 1958 Commercial Motor Show

National Museum of Science and Industry   Wroughton

Contact address: Exhibition Road, London SW7 2DD
Phone: 0207 942 4105
E-mail: s.evans@nmsi.ac.uk
Brief description: The bus collection is located at Wroughton airfield (hangar 4), near Swindon, Wiltshire.
Events planned: Open days are held and details of these may be found in the enthusiast press.

Opening days/times: Open only on Transport Festival and Open Days.
Directions by car: On A4361 approx 4 miles south of Swindon.
Directions by public transport: Publicised for Open Days
Charges: Published for each event.

Registration	Date	Chassis	Body	New to	Fleet No	Status
LMJ 653G	1913	Fiat 52B		(operator unknown) Yugoslavia		RP
JCP 60F	1928	Leyland Lion PLSC1	Leyland B31F	Jersey Railways & Tramways		A
DR 4902	1929	Leyland Titan TD1	Leyland L51RO	National Omnibus & Transport Co	2849	A
DX 8871+	1930	Ransomes Sims & Jefferies D	Ransomes Sims & Jefferies B31D	Ipswich Corporation	44	A
GW 713	1931	Gilford 1680T	Weymann C30D	Vallient of Ealing		A
VO 6806	1931	AEC Regal 662	Cravens B32F	Red Bus of Mansfield		A
JN 5783	1935	AEC Q 762	(chassis only)	Westcliff-on-Sea Motor Services		A
CPM 61+	1939	AEC 661T	Weymann H28/26R	Brighton Hove & District	6340	A
FR 1347	1940	Saurer CRD		GFM (Switzerland)	52	A
DHR 192	1943	Guy Arab II	Weymann UH30/26R	Swindon Corporation	51	A
KPT 909	1949	Leyland Titan PD2/1	Leyland L27/26R	Weardale Motor Services of Frosterley		R
LTA 772	1951	Bristol LWL5G	ECW B32R	Western National Omnibus Co	1613	A
HET 513	1953	Crossley DD42/7	Crossley H30/26R	Rotherham Corporation	213	A
NLP 645	1953	AEC Regal IV 9822E	Park Royal RDP37C	British European Airways	1035	A
OTT 55	1953	Bristol LS5G	ECW B41F	Southern National Omnibus Co	1701	A
OLJ 291	1954	Bedford CAV	Bedford B12	Non-psv use		A
VLT 140	1960	AEC Routemaster R2RH	Park Royal H36/28R	London Transport	RM140	R
504 EBL	1963	Bedford VAL 14	Duple C52F	Reliance Motor Services of Newbury	87	A
note u	1970	Moulton MD	Moulton C23F	Moulton Development vehicle		A
BCD 820L	1973	Leyland National 1151/1R/0102	Leyland National B49F	Southdown Motor Services	20	A
+ Trolleybus						

Notes:

LMJ 653G	Yugoslavia	FR 1347	Displays original Swiss registration FR1347
JCP 60F	Originally registered J 4601	note u	Eight wheeled integral development vehicle (unregistered)

Many buses at Wroughton are unrestored and in original condition. Seen here are former Swindon utility Guy Arab II/Weymann No 51 and all-Leyland TD1 National 2849.
Philip Lamb

North of England Open Air Museum   Beamish

Contact address: Beamish, Co Durham, DH9 0RG
Phone: 0191 370 4000
Fax: 0191 370 4001
E-mail: museum@Beamish.org.uk
Brief description: Beamish is an open-air museum which vividly recreates life in the North of England in the 19th and early 20th century. Buildings from throughout the region have been brought to Beamish, rebuilt and furnished as they once were. Costumed staff welcome visitors and demonstrate the past way of life in The Town, Colliery Village, Home Farm, Railway Station, Pockerley Manor and 1825 Railway. A one-mile circular period tramway carries visitors around the Museum and a replica 1913 Daimler bus operates between The Town and Colliery Village.
Events planned: (transport related, please contact for non-related events)
5 May 2002 — Power from the Past
11/12 May 2002 — Steam Glorious Steam
19 May 2002 — Morgan Car Meeting
22/23 June 2002 — History of Meccano
29/30 June 2002 — All Rover Car Rally

13/14 July 2002 — Vintage Collections Weekend
22 Sept 2002 — Classic car day
Opening days/times:
Summer: 23 March to 27 October: 10.00 to 17.00 (open every day)
Winter 28 October to 4 April 2003: 10.00 to 16.00 (closed Mondays and Fridays); also closed 16 December to 1 January (inclusive). Reduced operations in winter.
Last admission always 15.00.
Directions by car: Follow A1(M) to junction 63 (Chester-le-Street exit). Take A693 towards Stanley and follow Beamish Museum signs.
Directions by public transport: Buses 709 from Newcastle, 720 from Durham and 775/778 from Sunderland all serve Beamish.
Charges: — 2002 rates
Summer: Adult £12, Child £6, Over 60s £9.
Winter: £4 per person.
Group rates available for parties of 20 or more.
Facilities: B E F G H M P R T
Other information: Beamish is not ideal for wheelchair users. Free leaflet available in advance for visitors with disabilities and mobility limitations.

Registration	Date	Chassis	Body	New to	Fleet No	Status
WT 7108+	1924	Straker Clough T29	Brush B32F	Keighley Corporation Tramways	12	A
UP 551	1928	SOS QL	Brush Replica B37F	Northern General Transport Co	338	RP
VK 5401	1931	Dodge UF30A	Robson B14F	Baty of Rookhope		A
LTN 501+	1948	Sunbeam S7	Northern Coach Builders H39/31R	Newcastle Corporation	501	R
J 2503	1988	Renault	Osborne O18/14RO	Beamish of the North of England Open Air Museum		R

+ Trolleybus

Notes:
UP 551   Replica body in the course of construction
J 2503   Replica of 1913 Daimler.

Nottingham Transport Heritage Centre — Ruddington

Contact address: Mere Way, Ruddington, Nottingham NG11 6NX
Phone: 0115 940 5705
E-mail: aecley@aol.com
Affiliation: NARTM
Brief description: The centre offers exhibits covering road and rail transport along with steam road vehicles, and provides the opportunity to experience travel of a bygone age.
Events planned: Please see enthusiast press for details.

Opening days/times: Easter to mid-October: Sundays and Bank Holiday Mondays.
Directions by car: 3 miles south of Nottingham just off A52 ring-road and main A60 road via small roundabout at Ruddington.
Directions by public transport: Buses from Nottingham pass near museum
Charges: Not finalised at time of publication.
Facilities: B B(e) D E G H P R S T

Registration	Date	Chassis	Body	New to	Fleet No	Status
W 963	1923	Daimler CJA	Barton Ch22	Barton Transport of Chilwell		R
VO 8846	1932	Leyland Lion LT5	Willowbrook DP32F	South Notts Bus Co of Gotham	17	A
CRR 819	1947	Leyland Cub KPZ2	Brush C20F	Barton Transport of Chilwell	284	RP
DJF 349	1947	Leyland Titan PD1	Leyland H30/26R	Leicester City Transport	248	RP
JRR 930	1948	Leyland Titan PD1A	Duple L29/26F	Barton Transport of Chilwell	509	A
JVO 230	1948	Leyland Titan PD1A	Duple L29/26F	Barton Transport of Chilwell	507	R
MAL 310	1951	Leyland Royal Tiger PSU1/11	Duple DP45F	South Notts Bus Co of Gotham	42	A
APR 167A	1953	Leyland Titan PD2/12	Leyland H30/26RD	Barton Transport of Chilwell	732	A
NNN 968	1953	Leyland BTS1	Barton	Barton Transport of Chilwell	668	A
OTV 161	1953	AEC Regent III 9613E	Park Royal H30/26R	Nottingham City Transport	161	R
PFN 865	1959	AEC Regent V 2LD3RA		East Kent Road Car Co		R
851 FNN	1960	AEC Regent V 2D3RA	Northern Counties FL37/33F	Barton Transport of Chilwell	851	R
861 HAL	1960	Dennis Loline II	Northern Counties FL37/31F	Barton Transport of Chilwell	861	R
866 HAL	1960	AEC Reliance 2MU3RV	Plaxton C41F	Barton Transport of Chilwell	866	A
80 NVO	1962	Leyland Titan PD3/4	Northern Counties L33/32F	South Notts Bus Co of Gotham	80	RP
YRC 194	1962	Leyland Tiger Cub PSUC1/1	Alexander DP41F	Trent Motor Traction Co	194	RP
APA 46B	1964	AEC Reliance	Willowbrook B—F	Safeguard of Guildford		RP
CTT 518C	1965	AEC Regent V 2MD3RA	Willowbrook H33/28F	Devon General	518	RP
DAU 370C	1965	AEC Renown 3B3RA	Weymann H40/30F	Nottingham City Transport	370	R
ETO 452C	1965	Leyland Atlantean PDR1/1	Metro Cammell	Nottingham City Transport	452	RP
EOD 524D	1966	AEC Regent V 2D3RA	MCW H34/25F	Devon General	524	R
FEL 751D	1966	Bristol MW6G	ECW C39F	Hants & Dorset Motor Services	904	R
LNN 89E	1967	Albion Lowlander LR3	Northern Counties H41/30F	South Notts Bus Co of Gotham	89	RP
RCH 518F	1968	Daimler Fleetline CRG6LX	Alexander H44/33F	Trent Motor Traction Co	518	A
STO 523H	1970	Leyland Atlantean PDR1A/1	Northern Counties H47/30D	Nottingham City Transport	523	R
KVO 429P	1975	Leyland National 11351/2R	Leyland National B50F	Trent Motor Traction Co	429	A
ORC 545P	1976	Leyland Atlantean AN68/1R	ECW	Northern General Transport Co	3299	R
UFX 718	1979	AEC Reliance 6U2R	Plaxton C53F	London Country Bus Services	RS136	R
GTX 761W	1980	Bristol LHS6L	ECW DP27F	National Welsh Omnibus Services	MD8026	R
SCH 117X	1981	Leyland Fleetline FE30ALR	ECW H44/31F	South Notts Bus Co of Gotham	117	R
VRC 612Y	1981	Leyland Leopard PSU3G/4R	Plaxton C53F	Barton Transport of Chilwell	612	RP

Notes:

APR 167A	Originally registered RAL334
PFN 865	Recovery vehicle
861 HAL	Carries ultra-low-height 12ft 6in body
LNN 89E	Last Albion Lowlander delivered; badged Leyland
KVO 429P	Originally B44D
ORC 545P	Originally H45/27D and registered MPT299P; used as promotional vehicle
UFX 718	Originally registered EPM 136V

Above right: **Away from its home territory at the Nottingham Heritage Transport Centre, Ruddington is ex-Devon General AEC Regent V/MCW No 524.** *Philip Lamb*

Note: Please be aware that vehicles on display can vary from time to time as not all museums display their entire 'fleet'. Visitors wishing to see a particular vehicle should make enquiries prior to their visit.

Oxford Bus Museum

Long Hanborough

Contact address: Station Yard, Long Hanborough, Witney, Oxfordshire, OX29 8LA
Phone: 01993 883617 (Answerphone) or 01865 400002
Affiliation: NARTM
Brief description: Over 30 buses dating from 1915 to 1986, mainly from City of Oxford Motor Services and other local companies. The collection includes many vehicles of AEC manufacture.
Events planned: Please see enthusiast press for details.
Opening days/times: Sundays and Bank Holiday Mondays, 10.30 to 16.30. Saturdays open from Easter until the last Saturday in October, 13.30-16.30. Bus rides at 15.00 on the first Sunday of each month from the first Sunday in April to the first Sunday in October inclusive.

Directions by car: The entrance is on the south side of the A4095 (Witney-Bicester), between the villages of Bladon and Long Hanborough.
Directions by public transport: Museum is adjacent to Hanborough railway station on the Oxford-Worcester line, Sunday train services (journey time Oxford 10mins, London Paddington 70mins). Stagecoach bus service from George Street Oxford, weekdays, hourly to Long Hanborough village centre (1 mile)
Charges: Adults £2, Children/OAP £1.00, Family (2+2) £5.
Facilities: B(e) D P R S T
Other information: School parties welcome by arrangement — please telephone in advance.

Registration	Date	Chassis	Body	New to	Fleet No	Status
DU 4838	1915	Daimler Y	City of Oxford Electric Tramways B32R	City of Oxford Electric Tramways	39	RP
note e	1916	Daimler Y	(chassis only)			A
note f	1916	Daimler Y	(chassis only)			A
FC 2602	1917	Daimler Y	O18/16RO	City of Oxford Electric Tramways	46	A
JO 5032	1932	AEC Regal 642	no body	City of Oxford Motor Services	GC41	A
JO 5403	1932	AEC Regent 661	Brush O28/24R	City of Oxford Motor Services	GA16	RP
HA 8047	1933	SOS REDD	Metro Cammell H26/26R	BMMO ('Midland Red')	1047	RP
JVF 528	1949	Bedford OB	Duple C29F	Bensley of Martham		
NJO 703	1949	AEC Regal III 9621A	Willowbrook DP32F	City of Oxford Motor Services	703	R
OFC 393	1949	AEC Regent III 9612A	Weymann H30/26R	City of Oxford Motor Services	H892	A
OFC 205	1950	AEC Regal III 6821A	Duple C32F	South Midland Motor Services	66	A
PWL 413	1950	AEC Regent III 9613A	Weymann L27/26R	City of Oxford Motor Services	L166	RP

Registration	Date	Chassis	Body	New to	Fleet No	Status
GJB 254	1952	Bristol LWL6B	ECW B39R	Thames Valley Traction Co	616	A
SFC 609	1952	AEC Regal IV 9821S	Willowbrook C37C	City of Oxford Motor Services	609	A
SFC 610	1952	AEC Regal IV 9821S	Willowbrook C37C	City of Oxford Motor Services	610	RP
TWL 928	1953	AEC Regent III 9613S	Park Royal H30/26R	City of Oxford Motor Services	H928	RP
956 AJO	1957	AEC Regent V MD3RV	Park Royal H33/28R	City of Oxford Motor Services	H956	R
YNX 478	1958	AEC Reliance MU3RA	Duple Midland B44F	Chiltern Queens of Woodcote		RP
756 KFC	1960	AEC Reliance 2MU3RV	Park Royal B44F	City of Oxford Motor Services	756	R
14 LFC	1961	Morris FF	Wadham C27F	Morris Motors		A
304 KFC	1961	Dennis Loline II	East Lancs H35/28F	City of Oxford Motor Services	304	RP
305 KFC	1961	Dennis Loline II	East Lancs H35/28F	City of Oxford Motor Services	305	R
850 ABK	1962	AEC Reliance 2MU3RA	Duple C43F	Don Motor Coach Co of Southsea		RP
YWB 494M	1964	International Harvester 1853FC	Superior of Ohio B44F	United States Air Force		
AD 7156	1966	AEC Regent V 2D2RA	Metal Sections H51/39D	Kowloon Motor Bus	A165	A
FWL 371E	1967	AEC Renown 3B3RA	Northern Counties H38/27F	City of Oxford Motor Services	371	RP
NAC 416F	1967	Leyland Atlantean PDR1A/1	Northern Counties H44/31F	Stratford-upon-Avon Blue Motors	10	RP
UFC 430K	1971	Daimler Fleetline CRL6	Northern Counties H43/27D	City of Oxford Motor Services	430	A
EUD 256K	1972	AEC Reliance 6MU4R	Plaxton B47F	Chiltern Queens of Woodcote		A
VER 262L	1972	AEC Reliance 2U3ZR	Alexander C53F	Premier Travel of Cambridge	262	A
HUD 476S	1977	Bristol VRTSL3/6LXB	ECW H43/27D	City of Oxford Motor Services	476	R
UKE 830X	1982	Leyland Leopard PSU3G/4R	ECW C49F	East Kent Road Car Co	8830	A
A869 SUL	1983	Leyland Titan TNLXB/2RRSP	Leyland H44/26D	London Transport	T869	A
B106 XJO	1985	Ford Transit 160D	Dormobile B16F	South Midland	SM6	RP
C724 JJO	1986	Ford Transit	Carlyle DP20F	City of Oxford Motor Services		
D122 PTT	1987	Ford Transit 190D	Mellor B16F	Thames Transit	122	R

Notes:

DU 4838	Body new 1920		305 KFC	Sectioned museum display showing body construction method
note e	Chassis only			
note f	Chassis only		14 LFC	Originally used for Morris Motors band
FC 2602	Body ex-London built 1906		850 ABK	Acquired by Chiltern Queens of Woodcote in 1964
JO 5032	Passed to Mascot Motors in Jersey and subsequently conv. to lorry. Body removed. To be exhibited as chassis.		YWB 494M	Original USA Registration 64 B 2428
			AD 7156	Hong Kong registration
JO 5403	Originally H28/24R		NAC 416F	Acquired by City of Oxford Motor Services (905) in 1970
HA 8047	Sole surviving SOS double decker		A869 SUL	Acquired by City of Oxford Motor Services (975) in 1993
YNX 478	Carries 1956 body transferred from Dennis Pelican chassis			

St Helens Transport Museum

Contact address: The Old Bus Depot, 51 Hall Street, St Helens, WA10 1DU
Phone: 01744 451681
E-mail: E-mail@sthelens-transport-museum.co.uk
website: www.sthelens-transport-museum.co.uk
Affiliation: NARTM
Brief description: A collection of over 100 historic vehicles representing the transport heritage of the northwest of England. There is also a small exhibits section containing ticket machines, uniforms, signs and other transport-related items.
Events planned: Please see the enthusiast press for details
Opening days/times: Museum building currently under restoration. Expected to be open to the public from Easter 2003.
Facilities: A B(e) D G T

Registration	Date	Chassis	Body	New to	Fleet No	Status
ED 6141	1930	Leyland Titan TD1	Massey H28/26R	Warrington Corporation	22	A
KR 1728	1930	Leyland Titan TD1	Short H48R	Maidstone & District Motor Services	321	A
KJ 2578	1931	Leyland Titan TD1	Weymann	Redcar Motor Services of Tunbridge Wells		A
AFY 971	1934	Leyland Titan TD3	English Electric O26/25R	Southport Corporation	43	A
ATD 683	1935	Leyland Lion LT7	Massey B30R	Widnes Corporation	39	A
RV 6360	1935	Leyland Titan TD4	English Electric O26/24R	Portsmouth Corporation	117	RP
FTB 11	1942	Leyland Titan TD7	Northern Coach Builders UL27/26R	Leigh Corporation	84	A

Among the many varied buses at St Helens Transport Museum are these former SYPTE Leyland PD3s, both of which have been converted to towing tenders. They are seen here revisiting their home territory at Sheffield's Meadowhall shopping centre. *Ian McInnes*

Registration	Date	Chassis	Body	New to	Fleet No	Status
DKY 713+	1945	Karrier W	East Lancs H37/29F	Bradford Corporation	713	A
EWM 358	1945	Daimler CWA6	Duple UH30/26R	Southport Corporation	62	A
ANQ 778	1946	AEC Regent III	Commonwealth Engineering	Dept of Road Transport & Tramways of Sydney	1984	A
ARN 392	1946	Leyland Titan PD1A	Leyland H30/26R	Preston Corporation	88	RP
DED 797	1946	Leyland Titan PD1	Alexander H30/26R	Warrington Corporation	16	A
HLW 159	1946	AEC Regent III O961 RT	Park Royal H30/26R	London Transport	RT 172	R
EED 8	1947	Leyland Titan PD1	Alexander H30/26R	Warrington Corporation	24	R
FFY 401	1947	Leyland Titan PD2/3	Leyland O30/26R	Southport Corporation	84	A
FFY 403	1947	Leyland Titan PD2/3	Leyland O30/26R	Southport Corporation	86	A
FFY 404	1947	Leyland Titan PD2/3	Leyland O30/26R	Southport Corporation	87	R
BCB 341	1948	Leyland Tiger PS1	Crossley B32F	Blackburn Corporation	8	A
DBU 246	1948	Leyland Titan PD1/3	Roe H31/25R	Oldham Corporation	246	R
KTD 768	1948	Leyland Titan PD2/1	Lydney L27/26R	Leigh Corporation	16	R
ACB 902	1949	Guy Arab II	Northern Coach Builders H30/26R	Blackburn Corporation	74	A
ACC 88	1949	Bedford OB	Duple C29F	Deiniolen Motors		A
CBV 431	1949	Guy Arab III	Crossley H30/26R	Blackburn Corporation	131	A
FBU 827	1949	Crossley DD42/8	Crossley H30/26R	Oldham Corporation	368	A
KTC 615	1949	Guy Arab III	Guy B33R	Accrington Corporation	10	A
BDJ 67	1950	AEC Regent III O961 RT	Park Royal H30/26R	St Helens Corporation	D67	R
EX 6644	1950	Crossley SD42/7	Yeates C35F	W J Haylett ('Felix Coaches') of Great Yarmouth		A
GFY 406	1950	Leyland Titan PD2/3	Leyland H30/26R	Southport Corporation	106	A
JND 629	1951	Leyland Titan PD2/3	Metro Cammell H32/26R	Manchester Corporation	3228	R
BDJ 808	1952	AEC Regent III O961 RT	Park Royal	St Helens Corporation	D8	A
NTF 466	1952	Daimler CVG5	Northern Counties B32F	Lancaster City Transport	466	R

Registration	Date	Chassis	Body	New to	Fleet No	Status
CDJ 878	1954	Leyland Titan PD2/9	Davies H30/26R	St Helens Corporation	E78	A
RFM 644	1954	Guy Arab IV	Guy/Park Royal H30/26R	Chester Corporation	4	A
LDN 96	1955	AEC Regent III 6812A	Roe H33/27RD	York Pullman Bus Co	67	RP
ONE 744+	1956	BUT 9612T	Burlingham H33/26R	Manchester Corporation	1344	R
434 BTE	1957	Crossley Regent V D3RV	East Lancs H31/28RD	Darwen Corporation	17	R
GDJ 435	1957	AEC Regent V MD3RV	Weymann H33/26R	St Helens Corporation	H135	A
KRN 422	1957	Leyland Titan PD2/10	Crossley H33/29R	Preston Corporation	31	R
453 AUP	1958	AEC Reliance	Plaxton B45F	Wilkinson Bros of Sedgefield	53	R
GEN 201	1958	Leyland Titan PD3/6	Weymann H41/32RD	Bury Corporation	201	R
HDJ 753	1958	AEC Regent V D3RV	Weymann H33/26R	St Helens Corporation	J153	R
FHF 456	1959	Leyland Atlantean PDR1/1	Metro Cammell H44/33F	Wallasey Corporation	6	A
KDJ 999	1959	AEC Regent V 2D3RA	East Lancs H41/32F	St Helens Corporation	K199	A
MSD 407	1959	Leyland Titan PD3/6	Alexander L35/32RD	Western SMT Co	AD1543	A
PFR 346	1959	Leyland Titan PD2/27	Metro Cammell FH35/28RD	Blackpool Corporation	346	A
LDJ 985	1960	Leyland Titan PD2A/27	Weymann H30/25RD	St Helens Corporation	K175	A
PBN 668	1960	Daimler CVG6-30	East Lancs H41/32F	Bolton Corporation	150	RP
562 RTF	1961	Leyland Titan PD2/40	East Lancs H37/28R	Widnes Corporation	31	R
WLT 991	1961	AEC Routemaster R2RH	Park Royal H36/28R	London Transport	RM 991	R
152 CLT	1962	AEC Routemaster R2RH	Park Royal H36/28R	London Transport	RM 1152	R
574 TD	1962	Guy Arab IV	Northern Counties H41/32R	Lancashire United Transport	110	R
OWJ 353A	1962	Leyland Titan PD3/4	Roe	Doncaster Corporation	175	R
OWJ 354A	1962	Leyland Titan PD3/4	Roe	Doncaster Corporation	176	R
PSJ 480	1962	Leyland Titan PD2A/27	Massey H37/27F	Wigan Corporation	35	RP
TRJ 109	1962	AEC Reliance 2MU3RV	Weymann B45F	Salford City Transport	109	RP
201 YTE	1963	Leyland Titan PD2/37	East Lancs O37/28F	Lancaster City Transport	201	R
6219 TF	1963	Guy Arab IV	Northern Counties H41/32R	Lancashire United Transport	135	R
TDJ 612	1963	AEC Reliance 2MU3RA	Marshall B45F	St Helens Corporation	212	R
4227 FM	1964	Bristol Lodekka FS6G	ECW H33/27RD	Crosville Motor Services	DFG157	R
8859 VR	1964	AEC Regent V 2D3RA	East Lancs Neepsend H41/32R	A Mayne & Son of Manchester		R
AJA 139B	1964	Bedford VAL 14	Strachan B52F	North Western Road Car Co	139	RP
HTF 644B	1964	Leyland Titan PD2/40	East Lancs H37/28R	Widnes Corporation	38	R
HTJ 521B	1964	Guy Arab V	Northern Counties H41/32F	Lancashire United Transport	165	RP
JTD 300B	1964	Guy Arab V	Northern Counties H41/32F	Lancashire United Transport	166	A
BCK 367C	1965	Leyland Titan PD3/6	Leyland/Preston Corporation H38/32F	Preston Corporation	61	A
BED 731C	1965	Leyland Titan PD2/40 Special	East Lancs H34/30F	Warrington Corporation	50	R
CFR 590C	1965	Leyland Titan PD3A/1	Metro Cammell H41/30R	Blackpool Corporation	390	R
FFM 135C	1965	Guy Arab V	Massey H41/32F	Chester Corporation	35	A
FFM 136C	1965	Guy Arab V	Massey H41/32F	Chester Corporation	36	R
XTF 98D	1966	Leyland Titan PD3/4	East Lancs H41/32F	Haslingden Corporation	45	A
MDJ 554E	1967	Leyland Titan PD2A/27	East Lancs H37/28R	St Helens Corporation	54	R
MDJ 555E	1967	Leyland Titan PD2A/27	East Lancs H37/28R	St Helens Corporation	55	A
HCK 204G	1968	Leyland Panther PSUR1A/1R	MCW B47D	Preston Corporation	204	RP
KJA 299G	1968	Bristol RESL6G	Marshall B43F	North Western Road Car Co	299	R
LFR 529F	1968	Leyland Titan PD3/11	Metro Cammell H41/30R	Blackpool Corporation	529	RP
AFM 103G	1969	Bristol RELH6G	ECW C47F	Crosville Motor Services	CRG103	RP
AFM 106G	1969	Bristol RELH6G	ECW C47F	Crosville Motor Services	CRG106	R
DFM 347H	1969	Guy Arab V	Northern Counties H41/32F	Chester Corporation	47	RP
JFM 650J	1970	Daimler Fleetline CRG6LX	Northern Counties H43/29F	Chester Corporation	50	RP
SRJ 328H	1970	Leyland Atlantean PDR2/1	MCW H47/31D	SELNEC PTE	1205	RP
DKC 305L	1972	Leyland Atlantean AN68/1R	Alexander H43/32F	Merseyside PTE	1305	RP
JDJ 260K	1972	AEC Swift 3MP2R	Marshall B44D	St Helens Corporation	260	R
JMA 413L	1972	Bristol RELH6L	ECW C49F	North Western Road Car Co	413	R
PDJ 269L	1972	AEC Swift 3MP2R	Marshall B42D	St Helens Corporation	269	RP
RTC 645L	1972	Leyland National 1151/1R/0101	Leyland National B52F	Widnes Corporation	1	R
LED 71P	1976	Bristol RESL6G	East Lancs B41D	Warrington Corporation	71	R
LTE 489P	1976	Leyland Leopard PSU3D/2R	Plaxton B48F	Lancashire United Transport	438	R
VBA 151S	1978	Leyland Atlantean AN68A/1R	Northern Counties H43/32F	Greater Manchester PTE	8151	R

Registration	Date	Chassis	Body	New to	Fleet No	Status
XLV 140W	1980	Leyland National 2 NL116AL11/1R	Leyland National B49F	Merseyside PTE	6140	R
ANA 551Y + Trolleybus	1982	Leyland Atlantean AN68D/1R	Northern Counties H43/32F	Greater Manchester PTE	8551	RP

Notes:

KJ 2578	Originally H24/24R; converted to canteen by Liverpool Corporation (CL4)
AFY 971	Originally H26/25R
RV 6360	Originally H26/24R; renumbered 6 following open-top conversion
DKY 713	Rebodied 1960
HLW 159	Acquired by Bradford City Transport (410) in 1958
FFY 404	Originally H30/26R
FFY 401	Originally H30/26R
FFY 403	Originally H30/26R
BDJ 808	Converted to breakdown vehicle by Harper Bros of Heath Hayes
PSJ 480	Originally registered JJP 502
OWJ 354A	Converted to Breakdown Vehicle
OWJ 353A	Originally registered 475 HDT; converted to breakdown vehicle by South Yorkshire PTE and renumbered M3
201 YTE	Originally H37/28F
BCK 367C	Rebuilt from Leyland PD2 by Preston Corporation
DFM 347H	Last Guy Arab delivered to a British operator

St Helens purchased new a number of pure RTs, ideal for use in the town due to their low overall height (14ft 4³/₄in). Preserved at St Helens is the former No 67. *Philip Lamb*

Sandtoft Transport Centre

Contact address: Belton Road, Sandtoft, Doncaster DN8 5SX
Phone: 01724 711391
E-mail: enquiries@sandtoft.org.uk
Web site: www.sandtoft.org.uk
Brief description: Home of the nation's trolleybuses
Events planned: 5/6 May 2002, 2-4 June 2002, Trolleyday 30 June 2002, Trolleyday 8 July 2002, Gathering Preview 27 July 2002, Sandtoft Gathering 28 July 2002, Trolleyday 11 August 2002, European Days 25/26 August 2002, Six Wheeler Sunday 15 September 2002, St leger Rally 20 October 2002

Opening days/times: 12.00 to 17.00 on the above dates
Directions by car: From M180 junction 2, take A161 southbound to Belton. Turn right and museum is 2 miles on right-hand side.
Directions by public transport: Free bus from Doncaster station at 13.30 on 24 April, 30 July, 28 August and 22 October (please telephone to check operation)
Charges: Adult £3.50, Child/Senior Citizen £2, Family £10
Facilities: A B(e) D E F G H L P R S T
Other information: Coach tours and private party visits can be accommodated at other times by prior arrangement

Registration	Date	Chassis	Body	New to	Fleet No	Status
KW xxx+	1929	English Electric A	English Electric B—F	Bradford Corporation	5xx	A
1425 P+	1932	Fabrique Nationale	Fabrique Nationale B26SD	Liege (Belgium)	425	RP
TV 9333+	1934	Karrier E6	Brush H64R	Nottingham City Transport	367	A
FW 8990+	1937	AEC 661T	Park Royal H30/26R	Cleethorpes Corporation	54	RP
FTO 614	1939	AEC Regent O661	-	Nottingham City Transport	802	R
964 H87+	1943	Vetra CB60	CTL B17D	Limoges (France)	5	R
GHN 574+	1944	Karrier W	East Lancs H39/31F	Bradford Corporation	792	R
GKP 511+	1944	Sunbeam W	Roe H34/28R	Maidstone Corporation	56	R
CDT 636+	1945	Karrier W	Roe H34/28R	Doncaster Corporation	375	RP
DKY 703+	1945	Karrier W	East Lancs H37/29F	Bradford Corporation	703	RP
DKY 706+	1945	Karrier W	East Lancs H37/29F	Bradford Corporation	706	R
GTV 666+	1945	Karrier W	Brush UH30/26R	Nottingham City Transport	466	RP
RC 8575+	1945	Sunbeam W	Park Royal UH30/26R	Derby Corporation	175	A
CVH 741+	1947	Sunbeam MS2	Park Royal H40/30R	Huddersfield Corporation	541	RP
EDT 703	1947	Leyland Titan PD2/1	Roe H34/28R	Doncaster Corporation	94	RP
HKR 11+	1947	Sunbeam W	Northern Coach Builders H30/26R	Maidstone Corporation	72	RP
JV 9901	1947	AEC Regent III O961 RT	Roe H31/25R	Grimsby Corporation	81	RP
JMN 727	1948	AEC Regent III O961	Northern Counties H30/26R	Douglas Corporation	63	R
KTV 493+	1948	BUT 9611T	Roe H31/25R	Nottingham City Transport	493	RP
BCK 939	1949	Leyland Titan PD1		Preston Corporation	6	RP
EKU 743+	1949	BUT 9611T	Roe H33/25R	Bradford Corporation	743	A
EKU 746+	1949	BUT 9611T	Roe H33/25R	Bradford Corporation	746	R
EKY 558	1949	Leyland Titan PD2/3	Leyland H33/26R	Bradford Corporation	558	RP
GDT 421	1949	Daimler CVD6	Roe L27/26R	Doncaster Corporation	112	A
LHN 784+	1949	BUT 9611T	East Lancs H37/29F	Bradford Corporation	834	R
ERD 152+	1950	Sunbeam S7	Park Royal H38/30RD	Reading Corporation	181	R
FET 618+	1950	Daimler CTE6	Roe H40/30R	Rotherham Corporation	44	A
GAJ 12+	1950	Sunbeam F4	Roe H35/26R	Tees-side Railless Traction Board	2	RP
GFU 692+	1950	BUT 9611T	Northern Coach Builders H38/26R	Cleethorpes Corporation	59	A
JWW 375+	1950	Sunbeam F4	East Lancs H37/29F	Bradford Corporation	845	A
JWW 376+	1950	Sunbeam F4	East Lancs H37/29F	Bradford Corporation	846	A
JWW 377+	1950	Sunbeam F4	East Lancs H37/29F	Bradford Corporation	847	A
KTV 506+	1950	BUT 9641T	Brush H38/32R	Nottingham City Transport	506	R
BDJ 87+	1951	BUT 9611T	East Lancs H30/26R	St Helens Corporation	387	RP
FKU 758+	1951	BUT 9611T	Weymann H33/26R	Bradford Corporation	758	A
KDT 393	1951	AEC Regent III 9613A	Roe H31/25R	Doncaster Corporation	122	R
MDT 222	1953	AEC Regal III 9621A	Roe B39F	Doncaster Corporation	22	RP
OTV 137	1953	AEC Regent III 9613E	Park Royal H30/26R	Nottingham City Transport	137	RP
JDN 668	1954	AEC Regent III 6812A	Roe H33/25RD	York Pullman Bus Co	64	R
TDH 914+	1955	Sunbeam F4A	Willowbrook H36/34RD	Walsall Corporation	864	A
KVH 219+	1956	BUT 9641T	East Lancs H40/32R	Huddersfield Corporation	619	R
XWX 795	1959	AEC Reliance 2MU3RV	Roe C—F	Felix Motors of Doncaster	40	RP
9629 WU	1960	AEC Reliance 2MU3RV	Roe DP41F	Felix Motors of Doncaster	41	R
KSK 270+	1960	Saurer SWR Chassisless	Schindler B27T	Lucerne (Switzerland)	227	R

Registration	Date	Chassis	Body	New to	Fleet No	Status
VRD 193+	1961	Sunbeam F4A	Burlingham H38/30F	Reading Corporation	193	RP
657 BWB	1962	Leyland Atlantean PDR1/1	Park Royal H44/33F	Sheffield Joint Omnibus Committee	1357	R
433 MDT	1963	Leyland Tiger Cub PSUC1/11	Roe B45F	Doncaster Corporation	33	R
KHC 369	1963	AEC Regent V 2D3RV	East Lancs H32/28RD	Eastbourne Corporation	69	R
JTF 920B	1964	AEC Reliance 2MU3RV	East Lancs B—D	Reading Corporation	48	A
KDT 206D	1966	Daimler CVG6LX	Roe H34/28F	Doncaster Corporation	206	A
66+	1967	Lancia	Dalfa H43/25D	Oporto (Portugal)	140	R
UDT 455F	1968	Leyland Royal Tiger Cub RTC1/2	Roe B45D	Doncaster Corporation	55	R
WWJ 754M	1973	Daimler Fleetline CRG6LXB	Park Royal H43/27D	Sheffield Transport	754	R
C45 HDT+	1985	Dennis Dominator DTA1401	Alexander H47/33F	South Yorkshire PTE	2450	R

+ Trolleybus

Notes:

KW xxx	Caravan conversion to be restored. From batch 561-571.	BCK 939	Converted to breakdown vehicle
		FET 618	Rebodied 1957 (formerly single-decker)
FTO 614	Converted to tower wagon.	JWW 376	Rebodied 1962; chassis ex-Mexborough & Swinton
964 H87	French registration.	JWW 375	Rebodied 1962; chassis ex-Mexborough & Swinton
GHN 574	Originally single-decker; rebodied 1958	GAJ 12	Rebodied 1964
GKP 511	Rebodied 1960	JWW 377	Rebodied 1962; chassis ex-Mexborough & Swinton
CDT 636	Rebodied 1955	KSK 270	Registration not carried
DKY 703	Rebodied 1960	657 BWB	Rebodied 1968; renumbered 227 in 1970 following dissolution of JOC
DKY 706	Rebodied 1960		
EDT 703	Originally Leyland body. Roe body 1955 ex-Trolleybus	JTF 920B	Caravan conversion; originally registered 5148 DP
HKR 11	On loan from Maidstone Borough Council	66	Portuguese registration.
LHN 784	Rebodied 1962; chassis new to Darlington	C45 HDT	Experimental vehicle; originally registered B450 CKW.

Sandtoft Transport Centre is home to an extensive number of working trolleybuses. Seen here is former Bradford 844, a visitor in 2001. This 1948 Sunbeam F4 was rebodied by East Lancs in 1962. *Tony Wilson*

Contact address: M90 Commerce Park, Lathalmond, Fife, KY12 OSJ

Phone: 01383 623380

E-mail: website: www.busweb.co.uk/svbm

Affiliation: NARTM

Brief description: The collection of over 160 buses was, in the main, operated or manufactured in Scotland, from the late 1920s to the early 1980s. Vehicles are generally owned by private individuals or groups. A fully-equipped workshop enables comprehensive restoration to be undertaken. The 42-acre site is a former Royal Navy depot.

Events planned: Open weekend — please see enthusiast press for details.

Opening days/times: Easter to end of September, Sundays 13.00 to 17.00

Directions by car: Use M90 junction 4. Take B914 Dollar road. Left B915 Dunfermline (2 miles). 2 miles to M90 Commerce Park on right.

Directions by public transport: Nearest bus/train Dunfermline. No public transport to site.

Charges: Sunday opening £2. Other charges apply for open weekend.

Facilities: B B(e) D E P R S T

Registration	Date	Chassis	Body	New to	Fleet No	Status
GE 2446	1928	Leyland Titan TD1	Leyland L27/24RO	Glasgow Corporation	111	R
RU 8678	1929	Leyland Lion PLSC3	Leyland B35F	Hants & Dorset Motor Services	268	A
SO 3740	1929	Leyland Tiger TS2	Alexander B32F	Scottish General (Northern) Omnibus Co	P63	R
note o	1934	Body only	Cowieson B—R	Scottish Motor Traction Co	B124	A
VD 3433	1934	Leyland Lion LT5A	Alexander B36F	Central SMT		R
AAA 756	1935	Albion Victor PK114	Abbott C20C	King Alfred Motor Services		R
WG 3260	1935	Leyland Lion LT5A	Alexander B35F	W Alexander & Sons	P705	A
ATF 477	1937	Leyland Tiger TS7T	Fowler B39F	Singleton of Leyland		A
AUX 296	1939	Sentinel-HSG	Cowieson B32R	Sentinel of Shrewsbury (demonstrator)		RP
WG 8107	1939	Leyland Tiger TS8	Alexander -	W Alexander & Sons	P528	R
WG 8790	1939	Leyland Tiger TS8	Alexander B39F	W Alexander & Sons	P573	A
ETJ 108	1940	Leyland Tiger TS11	Roe -	Leigh Corporation	79	A
HF 9126	1940	Leyland Titan TD7	Metro Cammell	Wallasey Corporation	74	A
DSG 169	1942	Leyland Titan TD5	Alexander L27/26R	Scottish Motor Traction Co	J66	R
CDR 679	1943	Guy Arab II	Duple UH30/26R	Plymouth Corporation	249	RP
JWS 594	1943	Guy Arab II	Duple/Nudd H31/24R	London Transport	G 77	R
GAL 967	1944	Bedford OWB	Duple C29F	Gash of Newark	B7	A
BRS 37	1945	Daimler CWD6	Duple H30/26R	Aberdeen Corporation	155	R
AWG 639	1946	AEC Regal I O662	Alexander C35F	W Alexander & Sons	A52	R
AWG 623	1947	AEC Regal I O662	Alexander C31F	W Alexander & Sons	A36	R
HFO659	1947	Guy Arab III	(chassis only)	Blackburn Corporation	78	R
XG 9304	1947	Leyland Titan PD1A	Northern Counties L27/26R	Middlesborough Corporation	52	A
AWG 393	1948	Guy Arab III	Cravens H30/26R	W Alexander & Sons	RO607	R
BMS 405	1948	Daimler CVD6	Burlingham C33F	W Alexander & Sons	D10	A
BWG 39	1948	Bedford OB	Scottish Motor Traction C25F	W Alexander & Sons	W218	RP
ESG 652	1948	Guy Arab III	Metro Cammell B35R	Edinburgh Corporation	739	R
GGA 670	1948	Foden PVSC6	Plaxton FC35F	Scottish Co-operative Wholesale Society of Glasgow		A
FSC 182	1949	Daimler CVG6	Metro Cammell H31/25R	Edinburgh Corporation	135	R
CWG 283	1950	Leyland Tiger PS1	Alexander C35F	W Alexander & Sons	PA181	RP
DCS 616	1950	Daimler CVD6	Massey O32/28RD	Hunter (A1) of Dreghorn	16A	R
EVA 324	1950	Guy Arab III	Guy B33R	Central SMT Co	K24	R
GVD 47	1950	Guy Arab III	Duple H31/26R	Hutchinson's Coaches of Overtown		RP
JWX 599	1950	Albion Victor FT39N	Scottish Aviation C31F	Poskitt of Whitley Bay		A
SJ 1340	1950	Bedford OB	Duple C29F	Gordon of Lamlash		RP
SS 7486	1950	Bedford OB	Duple C29F	Stark's Motor Services of Dunbar		A
SS 7501	1950	Bedford OB	Duple C29F	Fairbairn of Haddington		R
DGS 536	1951	Leyland Tiger PS1/1	McLennan C39F	A & C McLennan of Spittalfield		R
DGS 625	1951	Leyland Tiger PS1/1	McLennan C39F	A & C McLennan of Spittalfield		R
DMS 820	1951	Leyland Tiger OPS2/1	Alexander C35F	W Alexander & Sons	PB7	A
DMS 823	1951	Leyland Tiger OPS2/1	Alexander C35F	W Alexander & Sons	PB10	RP
DWG 526	1951	Leyland Royal Tiger PSU1/15	Leyland C41C	W Alexander & Sons	PC30	A

Registration	Date	Chassis	Body	New to	Fleet No	Status
MTE 639	1951	AEC Regent III 6812A	Weymann H33/26R	Morecambe & Heysham Corporation	77	R
BMS 222	1952	Leyland Royal Tiger PSU1/15	Alexander C41C	W Alexander & Sons	PC1	R
CYJ 252	1953	AEC Regent III 9613E	Alexander H32/26R	Dundee Corporation	137	R
FGS 59D	1953	Bedford SB	Mulliner B36F	Royal Navy		RP
NXP 506	1953	Bedford SB	Plaxton C33F	D Halley of Sauchie		R
CHG 541	1954	Leyland Tiger PS2/14	East Lancs B39F	Burnley Colne & Nelson	41	R
GM 6384	1954	Leyland Titan PD2/10	Leyland L27/28R	Central SMT Co	L484	A
LFS 480	1954	Leyland Titan PD2/20	Metro Cammell H34/29R	Edinburgh Corporation	480	R
FWG 846	1955	Bristol LS6G	ECW B45F	W Alexander & Sons	E11	RP
HRG 209	1955	AEC Regent V D2RV6G	Crossley H35/29R	Aberdeen Corporation	209	A
TYD 888	1955	AEC Reliance MU3RV	Duple C43F	Wakes of Sparkford		R
UFF 178	1955	AEC Regent V D2RV6G	Crossley H35/29R	Aberdeen Corporation	207	A
OFS 777	1957	Leyland Titan PD2/20	Metro Cammell H34/29R	Edinburgh Corporation	777	R
OFS 798	1957	Leyland Titan PD2/20	Metro Cammell H34/29R	Edinburgh Corporation	798	RP
OWS 620	1957	Bristol Lodekka LD6G	ECW H33/27R	Scottish Omnibuses	AA620	A
1252 EV	1959	Bristol MW5G	ECW DP41F	Eastern National Omnibus Co	488	R
J 1359	1959	Albion Victor FT39KAN	Reading B35F	Jersey Motor Transport Co	5	RP
SWS 671	1959	AEC Reliance 2MU3RV	Alexander C38F	Scottish Omnibuses	B671	R
SWS 715	1959	AEC Reliance 2MU3RV	Park Royal C41F	Scottish Omnibuses	715	A
EDS 320A	1960	AEC Routemaster R2RH	Park Royal H36/28R	London Transport	RM 606	A
EDS 50A	1960	AEC Routemaster R2RH	Park Royal H36/28R	London Transport	RM 560	R
RAG 578	1960	Daimler CVG6LX	Northern Counties FH41/32FT Hunter (A1) of Kilmarnock			RP
VSC 86	1960	Leyland Tiger Cub PSUC1/3	Weymann B47F	Edinburgh Corporation	86	R
WAJ 112	1960	Albion Nimbus NS3N	Plaxton C29F	Watson of Huntingdon		RP
XSL 945A	1960	Bristol MW6G	Alexander C41F	Western SMT Co	T1590	A

This Weymann-bodied Leyland Tiger Cub was No 86 in the Edinburgh fleet. *Tony Wilson*

Registration	Date	Chassis	Body	New to	Fleet No	Status
XSN 25A	1960	Bristol MW6G	Alexander C41F	Western SMT Co	T1591	A
EDS 288A	1961	AEC Routemaster R2RH	Park Royal H36/28R	London Transport	RM 910	R
JVS 541	1961	Leyland Tiger Cub PSUC1/2	Alexander C41F	Alexander (Fife)	FPD225	R
RAG 411	1961	Bristol Lodekka LD6G	ECW H33/27RD	Western SMT Co	1645	R
RCS 382	1961	Leyland Titan PD3A/3	Alexander L35/32RD	Western SMT Co	1684	R
UCX 275	1961	Guy Wulfrunian	Roe H43/32F	County Motors of Lepton	99	R
YSG 101	1961	Leyland Leopard PSU3/2R	Alexander B33T	Edinburgh Corporation	101	R
YYJ 914	1961	Leyland Tiger Cub PSUC1/2	Alexander C41F	Stark's Motor Services of Dunbar	H8	A
7424 SP	1962	AEC Reliance 2MU3RV	Alexander C41F	W Alexander & Sons (Fife) Ltd	FAC4	R
LDS 201A	1962	AEC Routemaster R2RH	Park Royal H36/28R	London Transport	RM 1607	R
NSJ 502	1962	AEC Reliance 2MU3RV	Alexander C41F	W Alexander & Sons (Northern)	NAC205	R
UCS 659	1963	Albion Lowlander LR3	Northern Counties H40/31F	Western SMT Co	N1795	R
AFS 91B	1964	AEC Reliance 4MU3RA	Alexander B53F	Eastern Scottish	B91	R
ARG 17B	1964	AEC Reliance 2MU3RA	Alexander C41F	W Alexander & Sons (Northern) Ltd	NAC246	RP
ASC 665B	1964	Leyland Titan PD3/6	Alexander H41/29F	Edinburgh Corporation	665	R
AWA 124B	1964	Bedford SB13	Duple C41F	J O Andrew of Sheffield		R
BXA 452B	1964	Bristol Lodekka FS6G	ECW H33/27RD	W Alexander & Sons (Fife) Ltd	FAC4	R
BXA 464B	1964	Bristol Lodekka FS6G	ECW H33/27RD	W Alexander & Sons (Fife) Ltd	FRD199	R
CSG 29C	1965	Bristol Lodekka FLF6G	ECW -	Eastern Scottish		RP
ESF 801C	1965	Leyland Atlantean PDR1/1	Alexander H43/31F	Edinburgh Corporation	801	R
EWS 130D	1966	AEC Reliance 2U3RA	Alexander C—F	Eastern Scottish	ZB130	A
EWS 168D	1966	Bristol RELH6G	Alexander C38Ft	Scottish Omnibuses (Eastern Scottish)	XA168	A
FFV 447D	1966	AEC Reliance 2U3RA	Plaxton C45F	J Abbott & Sons of Blackpool		R
WTE 155D	1966	Guy Arab V	Northern Counties H41/30F	Lancashire United Transport	232	RP
GRS 343E	1967	Albion Viking VK43AL	Alexander DP40F	W Alexander & Sons (Northern) Ltd	NNV43	R
HDV 639E	1967	Bristol MW6G	ECW C39F	Western National Omnibus Co	1434	R
HGM 335E	1967	Bristol Lodekka FLF6G	ECW H44/34F	Central SMT Co	BL335	R
HGM 346E	1967	Bristol Lodekka FLF6G	ECW H44/34F	Central SMT Co	BL346	R
JSC 900E	1967	Leyland Atlantean PDR2/1	Alexander O47/35F	Edinburgh Corporation	900	R
KPM 91E	1967	Bristol Lodekka FLF6G	ECW O32/28F	Brighton Hove & District	91	R
LUS 524E	1967	AEC Reliance 2U3RA	Willowbrook C49F	David MacBrayne of Glasgow	150	R
NMY 634E	1967	AEC Routemaster R2RH/2	Park Royal H32/24F	British European Airways	8241	R
KGM 664F	1968	Leyland Leopard PSU3/1R	Alexander B53F	Central SMT Co	T64	A
NTY 416F	1968	AEC Reliance 6MU3R	Plaxton C45F	J Rowell of Prudhoe		RP
VMP 8G	1968	Albion Viking VK43AL	Alexander DP40F	Road Transport Industry Training Board	16	RP
NAG 120G	1969	Bristol REMH6G	Alexander C42Ft	Western SMT Co	T2214	RP
VMP 10G	1969	AEC Reliance 6U3ZR	Alexander B57F	Road Transport Industry Training Board	24	R
XFM 42G	1969	Guy Arab V	Northern Counties H41/32F	Chester Corporation	42	R
TMS 585H	1970	Leyland Leopard PSU3/1R	Alexander C49F	Road Transport Industry Training Board	84	RP
SXA 63K	1971	Daimler Fleetline CRG6LXB	Alexander H44/31F	W Alexander & Sons (Fife)	FRF63	A
TGM 214J	1971	Daimler Fleetline CRG6LX	ECW H43/34F	Central SMT Co	D14	RP
VFU 864J	1971	Bedford J2	Plaxton C—F	Hardings of Lincolnshire		RP
BFS 1L	1972	Leyland Atlantean AN68/1R	Alexander H45/30D	Edinburgh Corporation	1	R
BWG 833L	1972	Leyland Leopard PSU3/3R	Alexander B53F	W Alexander & Sons (Midland) Ltd	MPE133	A
BFS 463L	1973	Bedford YRQ	Alexander DP45F	Scottish Omnibuses (Eastern Scottish)	C463	A
BWS 105L	1973	Seddon Pennine IV-236	Seddon DP25F	Edinburgh Corporation	105	R

Above right: **McLennans, Spitalfield Leyland Tiger DGS 625 has stylish bodywork built in house.** *Tony Wilson*

Right: **Originally P528 in the Alexander fleet, this Leyland TS8 was later the subject of a very neat towing conversion.** *Tony Wilson*

Note: Please be aware that vehicles on display can vary from time to time as not all museums display their entire 'fleet'. Visitors wishing to see a particular vehicle should make enquiries prior to their visit.

Registration	Date	Chassis	Body	New to	Fleet No	Status
SCS 333M	1974	Leyland Leopard PSU3/3R	Alexander B53F	Western SMT Co	L2464	RP
SCS 366M	1974	Leyland Leopard PSU3/3R	Alexander B53F	Western SMT Co	L2497	R
LSX 16P	1975	Volvo Ailsa B57	Alexander H44/35F	Alexander (Fife)	FRA16	A
IIL 4595	1976	Bedford YRQ	Plaxton C45F	Reid & Mackay of Edinburgh		R
MSF 750P	1976	Seddon Pennine VII	Alexander C42Ft	Scottish Omnibuses (Eastern Scottish)	XS750	R
NCS 16P	1976	Leyland Fleetline FE30AGR	Alexander H43/31F	Hill (A1) of Stevenston		RP
ORS 60R	1977	Leyland Leopard PSU4C/4R	Alexander C45F	Grampian	60	R
OSJ 629R	1977	Leyland Leopard PSU3C/3R	Alexander B53F	Western SMT Co	L2629	RP
RRS 46R	1977	Leyland Leopard PSU3E/4R	Duple C49F	W Alexander & Sons (Northern)	NPE46	R
SMS 120P	1977	Daimler Fleetline CRG6LXB	Alexander H44/31F	W Alexander & Sons (Midland)	MRF120	RP
XMS 252R	1977	Leyland Leopard PSU3C/4R	Alexander B53F	W Alexander & Sons (Midland)	MPE252	A
CSG 773S	1978	Volvo Ailsa B55-10	Alexander H43/32F	Scottish Omnibuses (Eastern Scottish)	VV773	RP
CSG 792S	1978	Seddon Pennine VII	Plaxton C45F	Scottish Omnibuses (Eastern Scottish)	S792	RP
JSF 928T	1978	Seddon Pennine VII	Alexander DP49F	Scottish Omnibuses	S928	RP
NDL 656R	1978	Bristol VRTSL3/6LXB	ECW H43/31F	Southern Vectis Omnibus Co	656	RP
DSD 936V	1979	Seddon Pennine VII	Alexander C49F	Western SMT Co	S2936	RP
JSX 595T	1979	Leyland Atlantean AN68A/1R	Alexander H45/30D	Lothian Regional Transport	595	R
LIL 9929	1979	Bedford PJK	Plaxton C29F	Blood Transfusion Service		RP
SSX 602V	1979	Seddon Pennine VII	Alexander B53F	Scottish Omnibuses (Eastern Scottish)	S602	RP
WTS 266T	1979	Volvo Ailsa B55-10	Alexander H44/31D	Tayside Regional Council	266	R
ESF 647W	1980	Guy Victory Mk 2	Alexander H60/24D	China Motor Bus	LV36	R
RHS 400W	1980	Wales & Edwards	Wales & Edwards B12F	South of Scotland Electricity		R
VFS 542V	1980	Leyland Fleetline FE30AGR	Alexander H56/36D	China Motor Bus	SF31	R
FES 831W	1981	Volvo B58-61	Duple B59F	Stagecoach of Perth		R
GSC 658X	1981	Leyland Atlantean AN68A/1R	Alexander H45/30D	Lothian Regional Transport	658	A
HSC 173X	1981	Leyland Cub CU435	Duple B31F	Lothian Regional Transport	173	RP
GSC 667X	1982	Leyland Olympian ONTL11/1R	Alexander H47/28D	Lothian Regional Transport	667	R
NFS 176Y	1982	Leyland Leopard PSU3G/4R	Alexander C49F	W Alexander & Sons (Fife)	FPE176	RP
ULS 716X	1982	Leyland Leopard PSU3G/4R	Alexander C49F	W Alexander & Sons (Midland)	MPE416	RP
ULS 717X	1982	Leyland Leopard PSU3G/4R	Alexander C49F	W Alexander & Sons (Midland)	MPE417	RP

Notes:

SO 3740	Passed to W Alexander & Sons in 1930; numbered P63 in 1932 and rebodied in 1934
VD 3433	Rebodied 1945
WG 8107	Breakdown Vehicle. Originally C35F.
ETJ 108	Breakdown Vehicle
HF 9126	Originally H28/26R; acquired by Lancashire County Constabulary in 1952 and converted for use as mobile control post
DSG 169	Alexander body to Leyland design; converted to open-top in 1959 and restored in 1980/1
JWS 594	Originally London Transport G77 (GLL577); rebuilt and rebodied 1953
CDR 679	Orig Roe body converted to platform lorry in 1963. Present body from VV9135.
HFO659	Originally registered ACB907. Breakdown Vehicle.
SS 7486	Passed to Scottish Omnibuses (C22) in 1964
DCS 616	Rebodied in 1958 as H32/28RD
GVD 47	Acquired by McGill's Bus Services of Barrhead in 1952
FGS 59D	Originally registered 51 51 RN
UFF 178	Originally registered HRG207
EDS 320A	Originally registered WLT 606; acquired by Kelvin Scottish Omnibuses (1919) in 1986
EDS 50A	Originally registered WLT 560; acquired by Stagecoach at Perth in 1985
XSN 25A	Originally registered OCS 713
XSL 945A	Originally registered OCS 712
EDS 288A	Originally registered WLT 910; acquired by Kelvin Scottish Omnibuses (1929) in 1986
UCX 275	On loan from Dewsbury Bus Museum
YYJ 914	Originally registered ESS 989
NSJ 502	Originally registered SRS117.
LDS 201A	Originally registered 607 DYE; acquired by Stagecoach at Perth in 1986
CSG 29C	Converted to breaddown vehicle
NMY 634E	Passed to London Transport (RMA50) in 1979; acquired by Stagecoach at Perth in 1987
KPM 91E	Originally H38/32F; acquired by Scottish Omnibuses (AA971) in 1973 and converted to open-top (as OT2) in 1983
HDV 639E	First vehicle operated by Stagecoach
JSC 900E	Originally H47/35F
NDL 656R	Acquired by Lowland Scottish Omnibuses (856) in 1991
LIL 9929	Original identity unknown
ESF 647W	Original Hong Kong registration was CH 9399
VFS 542V	Originally registered CE2543 in Hong Kong
RHS 400W	Battery-electric bus
FES 831W	First new vehicle delivered to Stagecoach (as C50Ft)

Below left: **Alexander-bodied Leyland Royal Tiger coach PC1 was new in 1952.** *Tony Wilson*

Below: **Contrasting double-deck styles are provided by two former Western SMT machines. On the left is standard low-height Tilling-style Bristol LD6G 1645, with conventional lowbridge Leyland PD3A/3/ Alexander 1684 alongside.** *Tony Wilson*

Sheffield Bus Museum   Tinsley

Contact address: Tinsley Tram Sheds, Sheffield Road, Tinsley, Sheffield S9 2FY
Phone: 0114 255 3010
E-mail: website:
http://freespace.virgin.net/neil.worthington/sheff/page1~1.htm
Brief description: The display of over 20 vehicles is housed in part of a former tram shed.
Events planned: Please see enthusiast press for details.

Opening days/times: Open days as advertised; also most Saturdays and Sundays (not Christmas) 12.00 to 16.00 (please telephone to check opening times before travelling).
Directions by car: From M1 Junction 34 take A6178
Directions by public transport: By Supertram to Carbrook (200yd from museum); also good bus links from Sheffield and Rotherham.
Charges: Adult £1, concession 50p, Family £2.
Facilities: B(e)

Registration	Date	Chassis	Body	New to	Fleet No	Status
WG 9180	1940	Leyland Titan TD7	Leyland L27/26R	W Alexander & Sons	P266	R
GWJ 724	1941	AEC Regent O661	Sheffield Transport Department - Sheffield Corporation		G54	A
JWB 416	1947	Leyland Tiger PS1	Weymann B34R	Sheffield Corporation	216	A
HD 7905	1948	Leyland Tiger PS1	Brush B34F	Yorkshire Woollen District Transport Co	622	RP
KWE 255	1948	AEC Regent III 9612E	MCW	Sheffield Corporation	G55	A
MHY 765	1950	Leyland Comet ECPO/1R	Duple C32F	Orient Coaches of Bristol		RP
OWE 116	1952	AEC Regent III 9613A	Roe H33/25R	Sheffield Joint Omnibus Committee	116	A
KET 220	1954	Daimler CVG6	Weymann H30/26R	Rotherham Corporation	220	RP
RWB 87	1954	Leyland Titan PD2/12	Weymann H32/26R	Sheffield Corporation	687	RP
WRA 12	1955	AEC Monocoach MC3RV	Park Royal B45F	Booth & Fisher of Halfway		R
VDV 760	1958	Bristol Lodekka LD6G	ECW H33/27RD	Western National Omnibus Co	1943	A
PFN 858	1959	AEC Regent V 2LD3RA	Park Royal FH40/32F	East Kent Road Car Co		A
TDK 322	1959	AEC Regent V D2RA	Weymann H33/28RD	Rochdale Corporation	322	R
TET 135	1959	Daimler CVG6-30	Roe	Rotherham Corporation		RP
6330 WJ	1960	AEC Regent V 2D3RA	Roe H39/30RD	Sheffield Joint Omnibus Committee	1330	A
7874 WJ	1960	AEC Regent V 2D3RA	Alexander H37/32R	Sheffield Corporation	874	R
1322 WA	1961	AEC Reliance 2MU3RA	Plaxton C36F	Sheffield United Tours	322	A
GHD 765	1962	Leyland Titan PD3A/1	Metro Cammell H39/31F	Yorkshire Woollen District Transport Co	893	R
NAT 766A	1962	Daimler CVG6-30	Roe H39/31F	Grimsby - Cleethorpes Transport	57	RP
DWB 54H	1970	AEC Swift 5P2R	Park Royal B50F	Sheffield Transport	54	RP
AHA 451J	1971	Leyland Leopard PSU4B/4R	Plaxton C40F	BMMO ('Midland Red')	6451	A
LWB 383P	1976	Volvo Ailsa B55-10	Van Hool McArdle H44/31D	South Yorkshire PTE	383	R
LWB 388P	1976	Volvo Ailsa B55-10	Van Hool McArdle H44/31D	South Yorkshire PTE	388	RP
PSJ 825R	1976	Volvo Ailsa B55-10	Van Hool McArdle H44/31F	J Hunter (A1) of Kilmarnock		A

Notes:

GWJ 724	Originally bus 462; converted to grit wagon
KWE 255	Originally bus 255; converted to grit wagon
TET 135	Originally H39/31F; converted to breakdown vehicle
NAT 766A	Originally registered TJV 100
PSJ 825R	Originally H44/31D

Above right: **Exhibits at Sheffield Bus Museum include a Booth & Fisher AEC Monocoach and an SUT AEC Reliance.**

Seen at Birkenhead Docks is Iveco-engined AEC Routemaster KFF 367. The former RM1101 is resident at the Wirral Transport Museum. *Philip Lamb*

Part 2
Other Collections of Preserved Buses & Coaches

The Bristol Vintage Bus Group's former Western National Bristol K6A arrives at the Royal Victoria Country Park, Netley in 2000. *Philip Lamb*

Aldershot & District Bus Interest Group

Contact address: 111 Park Barn Drive, Guildford, Surrey, GU2 6ER
Web site: www.geocities.com/adbigweb
Affiliation: NARTM, FBHVC.
Brief description: The group was formed in 1994 to consolidate the collection of ex-Aldershot & District preserved vehicles and other artefacts which had been saved over the years. The vehicles range from 1920s Dennis E types to Dennis, AEC and Bristol buses which entered service in the 1960s and 1970s at the very end of the company's existence. The vehicles in the collection are in the care of

members of an associated group which also welcomes the owners of other preserved Dennis buses and coaches.
Events planned: Next running day 2 June 2002. Please see press for details.
Opening days/times: Running days are held from time to time at which many of the operational vehicles may be seen in service.
Other information: Regular working parties; new members welcome.

Registration	Date	Chassis	Body	New to	Fleet No	Status
OT 8283	1928	Dennis E	(chassis only)	Aldershot & District Traction Co	D210	A
OT 8592	1928	Dennis E	Strachan & Brown	Aldershot & District Traction Co	D217	A
OT 8898	1928	Dennis E	Strachan & Brown	Aldershot & District Traction Co	D226	A
RD 111	1928	Dennis G	(unknown) T17	Reading Fire Brigade		R
CC 8671	1929	Dennis GL	Roberts T19	Llandudno UDC		R
OU 1805	1929	Dennis E	(chassis only)	Aldershot & District Traction Co	D283	A
TE 7870	1929	Dennis ES	Brush B29D	Accrington Corporation	57	R
CC 9424	1930	Dennis GL	Roberts T20	Llandudno UDC		A
MJ 4549	1932	Dennis Lancet I	Short B32F	Smith of Westoning		R
TJ 836	1933	Dennis Dart	Duple C20F	Entwhistle of Morecambe		R
JG 8720	1937	Dennis Lancet II	Park Royal B35R	East Kent Road Car Co		RP
GAA 580	1948	Dennis Lancet J3	Strachan B32R	Aldershot & District Traction Co	944	A
GAA 616	1948	Dennis Lancet J3	Strachan C32R	Aldershot & District Traction Co	980	RP
GOU 845	1950	Dennis Lance K3	East Lancs L25/26R	Aldershot & District Traction Co	145	R
HOU 904	1950	Dennis Lancet J10	Strachan B38R	Aldershot & District Traction Co	178	R
LAA 231	1953	Dennis Lancet J10C	Strachan FC38R	Aldershot & District Traction Co	196	RP
LOU 48	1954	Dennis Lance K4	East Lancs L28/28R	Aldershot & District Traction Co	220	R
MOR 581	1954	AEC Reliance MU3RV	Metro Cammell B40F	Aldershot & District Traction Co	543	R
POR 428	1956	Dennis Falcon P5	Strachan B30F	Aldershot & District Traction Co	282	RP
SOU 456	1958	Dennis Loline	East Lancs H37/31RD	Aldershot & District Traction Co	348	RP
SOU 465	1958	Dennis Loline	East Lancs H37/31RD	Aldershot & District Traction Co	357	R
XHO 370	1960	AEC Reliance 2MU3RV	Weymann DP40F	Aldershot & District Traction Co	370	R
462 EOT	1962	Dennis Loline III	Alexander H39/29F	Aldershot & District Traction Co	462	RP
488 KOT	1964	Dennis Loline III	Weymann H39/29F	Aldershot & District Traction Co	488	R
AAA 503C	1965	Dennis Loline III	Weymann H39/29F	Aldershot & District Traction Co	503	R
AAA 506C	1965	Dennis Loline III	Weymann H39/29F	Aldershot & District Traction Co	506	R
AAA 508C	1965	Dennis Loline III	Weymann H39/29F	Aldershot & District Traction Co	508	RP
CCG 296K	1971	Bristol RESL6G	ECW B40D	Aldershot & District Traction Co	651	RP
KCG 627L	1973	Leyland National 1151/1R/0402	Leyland National B49F	Alder Valley	127	R

Notes:

OT 8283	Originally Dennis F converted to E type
RD 111	Replica body
TE 7870	Body rebuilt 1974 by Wyatt
JG 8720	Rebodied 1949
MOR 581	Rebodied 1967

Above right: **A long-standing member of the Aldershot & District Bus Interest Group's collection is Aldershot & District 145, A Dennis Lance K3 with lowbridge bodywork by East Lancs.** *Philip Lamb*

Right: **Dennis Loline III No 506 is one of four similar ex-Aldershot & District vehicles preserved. Bodywork is by Weymann.** *Philip Lamb*

Aycliffe & District Bus Preservation Society

Contact address: 110 Fewston Close, Newton Aycliffe, Co Durham, DL5 7HF
Affiliation: NARTM

Brief description: A collection of Darlington area service buses, the majority fully restored and in running order.
Opening days/times: Viewing by prior appointment only.

Registration	Date	Chassis	Body	New to	Fleet No	Status
GHN 189	1942	Bristol K5G	ECW L27/26R	United Automobile Services	BGL29	R
LHN 860	1950	Bristol L5G	ECW B35F	United Automobile Services	BG413	R
304 GHN	1958	Bristol LS6B	ECW C39F	United Automobile Services	BUC4	RP
AHN 451B	1964	Daimler CCG5	Roe H33/28R	Darlington Corporation	7	R
NDL 769G	1969	Bristol LHS6L	Marshall B35F	Southern Vectis Omnibus Co	833	R

Notes:

GHN 189	1949 body fitted in 1954
LHN 860	Converted to OMO c. 1957
304 GHN	Now fitted with Gardner engine. Was C34F when new.
NDL 769G	Acquired by United Automobile Services (1452) in 1977

Former Darlington Roe-bodied Daimler 7 is a rare CCG5 model. *Aycliffe & District Bus Preservation Society*

Bolton Bus Group

Contact address: 12 Arundale, Westhoughton, Bolton BL5 3YB
Brief description: A small group of enthusiasts formed to preserve examples of Bolton's buses. Some of the vehicles are displayed at

Bury Transport Museum, which can be visited by prior arrangement.
Opening days/times: Please write to the above address to arrange a visit

Registration	Date	Chassis	Body	New to	Fleet No	Status
NBN 436	1959	Leyland Titan PD3/4	East Lancs H41/32F	Bolton Corporation	128	RP
SBN 767	1961	AEC Regent V 2D3RA	Metro Cammell H40/32F	Bolton Corporation	167	A
FBN 232C	1965	Leyland Atlantean PDR1/1	East Lancs H45/33F	Bolton Corporation	232	R
KUS 607E	1967	Leyland Atlantean PDR1/1	Alexander H44/34F	Glasgow Corporation	LA352	RP
TWH 807K	1971	Leyland Atlantean PDR2/1	East Lancs H49/37F	SELNEC PTE	6807	A
TWH 809K	1971	Leyland Atlantean PDR2/1	East Lancs H49/37F	SELNEC PTE	6809	R

Notes:
TWH 807K   Playbus

Bournemouth Heritage Transport Collection

Phone: 01202 658333
Brief description: The collection comprises vehicles, mainly from Bournemouth Corporation or the Bournemouth area, built between the years 1928 and 1980. Most are owned by the Bournemouth Passenger Transport Association Ltd, which is a registered charity.

Events planned: Please see the enthusiast press for details
Opening days/times: Owing to storage relocation, the collection is not currently open to the public. It is hoped to arrange an event during 2002. Please see the enthusiast press for details

Registration	Date	Chassis	Body	New to	Fleet No	Status
RU 2266	1925	Shelvoke & Drewery Tramocar	no body	Bournemouth Corporation	9	A
LJ 500	1929	Karrier WL6/1	Hall Lewis B40D	Bournemouth Corporation	33	RP
VH 6188	1934	AEC Regent O661	Hall Lewis H26/24R	Huddersfield Corporation	119	A
VH 6217	1934	AEC Regent 661	Lee Motors -	Huddersfield Corporation	120	R
BOW 162	1938	Bristol L5G	Hants & Dorset -	Hants & Dorset Motor Services	9081	RP
DKY 711+	1944	Karrier W	East Lancs H37/29F	Bradford Corporation	711	A
DKY 712+	1944	Karrier W	East Lancs H37/29F	Bradford Corporation	712	A
HLJ 44	1948	Bristol K6A	ECW L27/28R	Hants & Dorset Motor Services	TD895	RP
JLJ 403	1949	Leyland Tiger PS2/3	Burlingham FDP35F	Bournemouth Corporation	46	R
KEL 110	1949	Leyland Titan PD2/3	Weymann FH33/25D	Bournemouth Corporation	110	R
NNU 234+	1949	BUT 9611T	Weymann H32/26R	Nottinghamshire & Derbyshire Traction Co	353	RP
KEL 127	1950	Leyland Titan PD2/3	Weymann FH33/25D	Bournemouth Corporation	127	A
KEL 133	1950	Leyland Titan PD2/3	Weymann FH27/21D	Bournemouth Corporation	247	R
KLJ 346+	1950	BUT 9641T	Weymann H31/25D	Bournemouth Corporation	212	R
MOD 978	1952	Bristol LS6G	ECW C41F	Southern National Omnibus Co (Royal Blue)	1291	A
NLJ 268	1953	Leyland Royal Tiger PSU1/13	Burlingham B42F	Bournemouth Corporation	258	R
NLJ 272	1953	Leyland Royal Tiger PSU1/13	Burlingham B42F	Bournemouth Corporation	262	R
RRU 901	1955	Leyland Tiger Cub PSUC1/1	Park Royal B42F	Bournemouth Corporation	264	R
RRU 904	1955	Leyland Tiger Cub PSUC1/1	Park Royal B42F	Bournemouth Corporation	267	R
YLJ 147	1959	Leyland Titan PD3/1	Weymann H37/25D	Bournemouth Corporation	147	R
8154 EL	1960	Leyland Titan PD3/1	Weymann H37/25D	Bournemouth Corporation	154	R
8156 EL	1960	Leyland Titan PD3/1	Weymann O37/25D	Bournemouth Corporation	156	R
8159 EL	1960	Leyland Titan PD3/1	Weymann H37/25D	Bournemouth Corporation	159	R
NMR 345	1960	Leyland Titan PD3/1	Weymann H37/25D	Bournemouth Corporation	155	RP
297 LJ+	1962	Sunbeam MF2B	Weymann H37/28D	Bournemouth Corporation	297	R
6162 RU	1963	Leyland Titan PD3A/1	Weymann H39/30F	Bournemouth Corporation	162	A
6167 RU	1963	Leyland Titan PD3A/1	Weymann H39/30F	Bournemouth Corporation	167	R
AEL 170B	1964	Leyland Atlantean PDR1/1	Weymann H43/31F	Bournemouth Corporation	170	R
ALJ 340B	1964	Daimler Fleetline CRG6LX	M H Cars H44/33F	Bournemouth Corporation	40	R
CRU 103C	1965	Leyland Leopard PSU3/2R	Weymann DP45F	Bournemouth Corporation	103	R
CRU 180C	1965	Daimler Fleetline CRG6LX	Weymann CO43/31F	Bournemouth Corporation	180	R

Registration	Date	Chassis	Body	New to	Fleet No	Status
CRU 187C	1965	Daimler Fleetline CRG6LX	Weymann CO43/31F	Bournemouth Corporation	187	R
ERV 247D	1966	Leyland Atlantean PDR1/1	MCW O43/33F	Portsmouth Corporation	247	RP
ERV 249D	1966	Leyland Atlantean PDR1/1	MCW O43/33F	Portsmouth Corporation	249	R
ERV 251D	1966	Leyland Atlantean PDR1/1	MCW O43/33F	Portsmouth Corporation	251	R
ERV 252D	1966	Leyland Atlantean PDR1/1	MCW O43/33F	Portsmouth Corporation	252	R
FJY 915E	1967	Leyland Atlantean PDR1/1	MCW O43/32F	Plymouth Corporation	215	RP
KRU 55F	1967	Daimler Roadliner SRC6	Willowbrook B49F	Bournemouth Corporation	55	R
ORU 230G	1969	Leyland Atlantean PDR1A/1	Alexander H43/31F	Bournemouth Corporation	230	R
VRU 124J	1971	Daimler Fleetline CRG6LXB	Roe H43/31F	Hants & Dorset Motor Services	1901	R
DLJ 111L	1972	Daimler Fleetline CRL6	Alexander O43/31F	Bournemouth Corporation	111	R
DLJ 116L	1972	Daimler Fleetline CRL6	Alexander H43/31F	Bournemouth Corporation	116	R
DLJ 119L	1972	Daimler Fleetline CRL6	Alexander H43/31F	Bournemouth Corporation	119	A
XRU 277K	1972	Leyland Atlantean PDR1A/1	Alexander H43/31F	Bournemouth Corporation	277	RP
FEL 105L	1973	Leyland Leopard PSU3B/4R	Plaxton C47F	Bournemouth Corporation	105	A
FEL 209V	1979	Dodge KCSK6055	Rootes B18F	Bournemouth Corporation	M9	A

+Trolleybus

Notes:

RU 2266	Believed only chassis & axles are from RU 2266	8159 EL	Converted to mobile museum
VH 6217	Converted to tower wagon in 1948	8156 EL	Converted to open top in 1991
VH 6188	Chassis new 1934 fitted with 1928 body	NMR 345	Originally registered 8155 EL
BOW 162	New with Beadle body; converted to breakdown vehicle	ERV 247D	Originally H43/33F
DKY 711	Rebodied 1960	FJY 915E	Originally H43/32F
DKY 712	Rebodied 1960	DLJ 111L	Originally H43/31F
NLJ 268	Originally B42F; used as canteen at Chesterfield 1970-81. Now mobile museum display vehicle.	FEL 209V	Battery powered bus

All three of these elegant ex-Bournemouth Burlingham-bodied Leyland Tigers survive. No 46 is with the Bournemouth Historic Transport Collection. *Philip Lamb*

Bristol Vintage Bus Group

Contact address: 74 Ridgeway Lane, Whitchurch, Bristol BS14 9PJ
Location: Unit G, Flowers Hill Road, Brislington, Bristol
Brief description: A small group of enthusiasts formed to preserve examples of Bristol's buses.
Events planned: Please see enthusiast press for details
Opening days/times: At any time by prior arrangement if someone is available

Directions by car: Flowers Hill Road is off the A4 Bath road, right on the City boundary near the Park & Ride
Directions by public transport: Main bus service to Bath from the Bus Station and Temple Meads railway station stops near Flowers Hill
Charges: No admission charge for viewing or special events

Registration	Date	Chassis	Body	New to	Fleet No	Status
AHU 803	1934	Bristol J5G	Brislington Body Works B35R	Bristol Tramways	2355	R
GHT 154	1940	Bristol K5G	Brislington Body Works H30/26R	Bristol Tramways	C3336	R
FTT 704	1945	Bristol K6A	ECW L27/28R	Western National Omnibus Co	353	R
LAE 13	1948	Leyland Titan PD1A	ECW H30/26R	Bristol Tramways	C4044	R
YHY 80	1957	Bristol LS6G	ECW B43F	Bristol Omnibus Co	3004	RP

Notes:
AHU 803   Rebodied 1947. Originally a petrol engined coach.
FTT 704   Original Strachans body replaced in 1955.

A very small number of ECW-bodied Leyland PD1/PD1As delivered to former Tilling fleets in the early postwar years survive. Bristol Tramways C4044, a PD1A is preserved with the Bristol Vintage Bus Group.
Philip Lamb

British Trolleybus Society

Contact address: 8 Riding Lane, Hildenborough, Tonbridge, Kent, TN11 9HX

Brief description: The British Trolleybus Society is a contributor society to the Sandtoft Transport Centre. Vehicles from the collection of trolleybuses can be seen from time to time at Sandtoft on display.

Events planned: Details given in the section on Sandtoft Transport Centre

Registration	Date	Chassis	Body	New to	Fleet No	Status
WW 4688+	1927	Garrett O type	Garrett B32C	Mexborough & Swinton Traction Co	34	A
ALJ 973+	1935	Sunbeam MS2	Park Royal H31/25D	Bournemouth Corporation	99	RP
RD 7127	1935	AEC Regent O661	Park Royal L26/26R	Reading Corporation	47	R
CU 3593+	1937	Karrier E4	Weymann H29/26R	South Shields Corporation	204	RP
ARD 676+	1939	AEC 661T	Park Royal H30/26R	Reading Corporation	113	R
CKG 193+	1942	AEC 664T	Northern Counties H38/32R	Cardiff Corporation	203	A
HYM 812+	1948	BUT 9641T	Metro Cammell H40/30R	London Transport	1812	R
NDH 959+	1951	Sunbeam F4	Brush H34/31R	Walsall Corporation	342	RP
AC-L 379+	1956	Henschel 562E	Ludewig RB17/44T	Aachen (Germany)	22	R
XDH 72+	1956	Sunbeam F4A	Willowbrook H36/34RD	Walsall Corporation	872	R
FYS 839+	1958	BUT 9613T	Crossley H37/34R	Glasgow Corporation	TB78	R
PVH 931+	1959	Sunbeam S7A	East Lancs H40/32R	Huddersfield Corporation	631	R

+Trolleybus

Notes:

NDH 959	Rebuilt/lengthened 1965
AC-L 379	German registration
XDH 72	Last Walsall trolleybus; on display at Aston Manor Road Transport Museum.

Cardiff & South Wales Trolleybus Project

Contact address: 211 Hillrise, Llanedeyrn, Cardiff CF23 6UQ

Affiliation: NARTM

Brief description: The only trolleybus preservation group in the principality of Wales. A regular newsletter is issued, and new members are always welcome.

Registration	Date	Chassis	Body	New to	Fleet No	Status
DKY 704+	1945	Karrier W	East Lancs H37/29F	Bradford Corporation	704	RP
EBO 919+	1949	BUT 9641T	Bruce H38/29D	Cardiff Corporation	262	RP
KBO 961+	1955	BUT 9641T	East Lancs B40R	Cardiff Corporation	243	A
DHW 293K	1972	Bristol LH6L	ECW B42F	Bristol Omnibus Co	353	

+Trolleybuses

Notes:

DKY 704	Rebodied 1959
EBO 919	Body built on East Lancs frames
DHW 293K	Support vehicle

Chelveston Preservation Society

Contact address: 36 Moor Road, Rushden, Northants, NN10 9SP

Brief description: The group has its origins with a small number of employees of United Counties. The collection has evolved to represent most types of Bristol chassis from a range of former Tilling group companies.

Registration	Date	Chassis	Body	New to	Fleet No	Status
VV 5696	1937	Bristol JO5G	ECW B35R	United Counties Omnibus Co	450	R
MPU 21	1948	Bristol K6B	ECW L27/28R	Eastern National Omnibus Co	3960	RP
HPW 108	1949	Bristol K5G	ECW H30/26R	Eastern Counties Omnibus Co	LKH108	RP

Registration	Date	Chassis	Body	New to	Fleet No	Status
NAE 3	1950	Bristol L6B	ECW FC31F	Bristol Tramways	2467	RP
ONO 995	1950	Bristol LL5G	ECW B39R	Eastern National Omnibus Co	4081	A
CNH 860	1952	Bristol LWL6B	ECW B39R	United Counties Omnibus Co	426	R
CNH 862	1952	Bristol LWL6B	ECW DP33R	United Counties Omnibus Co	428	R
HWV 294	1952	Bristol KSW5G	ECW L27/28R	Wilts & Dorset Motor Services	365	A
KNV 337	1954	Bristol KSW6B	ECW L27/28R	United Counties Omnibus Co	964	R
RFM 408	1954	Bristol Lodekka LD6B	ECW H33/25R	Crosville Motor Services	ML663	A
TUO 497	1956	Bristol LS6G	ECW B45F	Southern National Omnibus Co	1781	RP
VVF 543	1957	Bristol SC4LK	ECW B35F	Eastern Counties Omnibus Co	LC543	RP
RFU 689	1958	Bristol SC4LK	ECW DP33F	Lincolnshire Road Car Co	2611	R
OPN 807	1959	Bristol Lodekka LDS6B	ECW H33/27R	Brighton Hove & District	7	RP
675 COD	1960	Bristol SUS4A	ECW B30F	Western National Omnibus Co	603	A
264 KTA	1962	Bristol MW6G	ECW C39F	Western National Omnibus Co	1395	A
827 BWY	1963	Bristol MW6G	ECW B45F	West Yorkshire Road Car Co	SMG19	RP
375 GWN	1964	Bristol RELL6G	ECW C47F	United Welsh Services	52	A
ABD 253B	1964	Bristol RELH6G	ECW C47F	United Counties Omnibus Co	253	A
DEL 893C	1965	Bristol Lodekka FLF6G	ECW H38/32F	Hants & Dorset Motor Services	1523	A
GAX 2C	1965	Bristol RELL6G	ECW B54F	Red & White Services	R2 65	RP
EDV 555D	1966	Bristol SUL4A	ECW B36F	Southern National Omnibus Co	692	A
OWC 182D	1966	Bristol MW6G	ECW C34F	Tillings Transport	182	R
OAX 9F	1968	Bristol RELH6G	ECW C47F	Red & White Services	RC968	R
UFM 53F	1968	Bristol RELL6G	ECW DP50F	Crosville Motor Services	ERG53	
MMW 354G	1969	Bristol RELL6G	ECW B45D	Wilts & Dorset Motor Services	824	R
SGF 483L	1970	Bristol RELH6L	Plaxton C51F	Isle of Man Road Services	40	A
HAH 537L	1972	Bristol LH6P	ECW B45F	Eastern Counties Omnibus Co	LH537	RP
YFM 283L	1973	Bristol RELL6G	ECW DP50F	Crosville Motor Services	ERG283	RP
JFJ 506N	1975	Bristol LH6L	Plaxton C43F	Greenslades Tours	326	RP
AFJ 732T	1977	Bristol LH6L	Plaxton C43F	Western National Omnibus Co	3312	R
HBD 919T	1977	Bristol VRTSL6G	ECW H66F	United Counties Omnibus Co	919	R

Notes:

VV 5696	Rebodied 1949
CNH 862	Gardner 5LW engine fitted in 1956. Reverted to Bristol AVW in 1996.
CNH 860	Renumbered 426 in 1952; Gardner 5LW engine fitted 1956
RFM 408	Eighth production Lodekka. Currently has no engine or gearbox
OWC 182D	Passed to Eastern National (392) in 1968 and to Tilling's Travel (9392) in 1971
SGF 483L	Originally registered 40 WMN

A well-known member of the Chelveston Preservation Society collection is 1937 Bristol JO5G, United Counties No 450.
Geoff Mills

Cherwell Bus Preservation Group

Contact address: 17 Andersons Close, Kidlington, Oxford OX5 1ST
Brief description: A collection of mainly ex-City of Oxford vehicles housed under cover.

Events planned: The operational vehicles will attend a few events during the rally season.

Registration	Date	Chassis	Body	New to	Fleet No	Status
OJO 727	1950	AEC Regal III 9621A	Willowbrook B32F	City of Oxford Motor Services	727	R
191 AWL	1956	AEC Regent V MD3RV	Weymann L30/26R	City of Oxford Motor Services	L191	R
194 BFC	1957	AEC Regent V MD3RV	Weymann L30/28RD	City of Oxford Motor Services	L194	RP
975 CWL	1958	AEC Regent V LD3RA	Park Royal H37/28R	City of Oxford Motor Services	H975	RP
312 MFC	1961	AEC Bridgemaster 2B3RA	Park Royal H43/29F	City of Oxford Motor Services	312	RP
324 NJO	1962	AEC Bridgemaster 2B3RA	Park Royal H40/25F	City of Oxford Motor Services	324	RP
332 RJO	1963	AEC Renown 3B3RA	Park Royal H38/27F	City of Oxford Motor Services	332	RP
340 TJO	1964	AEC Renown 3B3RA	Park Royal H38/27F	City of Oxford Motor Services	340	A
OFC 902H	1970	Bristol VRTSL2/6LX	ECW H39/31F	City of Oxford Motor Services	902	RP
VUD 348H	1970	Leyland Leopard PSU3A/4R	Plaxton	Heyfordian of Upper Heyford		A
AUD 310J	1971	Leyland Leopard PSU3B/4R	Plaxton C51F	O A Slatter & Sons of Long Hanborough	40	A
TJO 56K	1971	AEC Reliance 6MU4R	Marshall DP49F	City of Oxford Motor Services	56	A
YWL 134K	1972	Leyland Leopard PSU3B/4R	Plaxton C53F	R Jarvis & Sons of Middle Barton		A
NUD 105L	1973	Bristol VRTSL2/6LX	ECW CH41/27F	City of Oxford Motor Services	105	A
RBW 87M	1974	Bristol RELH6L	ECW DP49F	City of Oxford Motor Services	87	A
PWL 999W	1980	Leyland Olympian B45 ONTL11/2R	Alexander H50/32D	Leyland (prototype)	OBC999	A
VJO 201X	1982	Leyland Olympian ONLXB/1R	ECW H47/28D	City of Oxford Motor Services	201	A
VUD 30X	1982	Leyland Leopard PSU3G/4R	ECW C49F	City of Oxford Motor Services	30	R
C729 JJO	1986	Ford Transit 190D	Carlyle DP20F	City of Oxford Motor Services	729	RP

Notes:
PWL 999W   Prototype operated by Singapore Bus registered SBS5396B. Acquired by COMS in 1987.

Above right: **One or two early ECW-bodied Leyland Olympians are now preserved. City of Oxford 201 is with the Cherwell Valley Bus Preservation Group.** *Philip Lamb*

Right: **The Chesterfield 123 group's fleet on display with a 'still in service' Leyland Fleetline of TM Travel.** *Chesterfield 123 Group*

Chesterfield 123 Group

Contact address: 3 Ash Grove, Mastin Moor, Chesterfield S43 3AW
Brief description: The group owns the small collection of Chesterfield vehicles listed, which are shown at rallies throughout the

season. However, former South Yorkshire PTE Fleetline 1515 has been added Collection. Meetings are held every other Wednesday at the Donkey Derby Freehouse, Whittington Moor, Chesterfield.

Registration	Date	Chassis	Body	New to	Fleet No	Status
PNU 114K	1971	Leyland Atlantean PDR1A/1	Northern Counties H44/28D	Chesterfield Corporation	114	RP
NNU 123M	1973	Daimler Fleetline CRL6-30	Roe H42/29D	Chesterfield Corporation	123	R
NNU 124M	1973	Daimler Fleetline CRL6-30	Roe H42/29D	Chesterfield Corporation	124	R
OKW 515R	1977	Leyland Fleetline FE30AGR	MCW H46/25F	South Yorkshire PTE	1515	A

Note:
OKW 515R   To be restored to H46/25D

Registration	Date	Chassis	Body	New to	Fleet No	Status
JHL 983	1957	AEC Reliance MU3RV	Roe C41C	West Riding Automobile Co	803	R
KHL 855	1957	Guy Arab IV	Roe L29/26RD	West Riding Automobile Co	855	RP
924 AHY	1958	Bristol MW5G	ECW B45F	Bristol Omnibus Co	2934	RP
TWT 123	1958	Bristol MW5G	ECW DP41F	West Yorkshire Road Car Co	EUG 71	RP
5228 NW	1959	Leyland Titan PD3/5	Roe H38/32R	Leeds City Transport	228	A
LEN 101	1960	Guy Wulfrunian	(chassis only)	Bury Corporation	101	A
574 CNW	1962	Daimler CVG6	Roe H39/31F	Leeds City Transport	574	RP
PJX 35	1962	Leyland Leopard L1	Weymann B42F	Halifax Corporation	35	R
WHL 970	1963	Guy Wulfrunian	Roe H43/32F	West Riding Automobile Co	970	A
CUV 208C	1965	AEC Routemaster R2RH	Park Royal H36/28R	London Transport	RM2208	R
LHL 164F	1967	Leyland Panther PSUR1/1	Roe B51F	West Riding Automobile Co	164	R
NWW 89E	1967	Leyland Leopard L1	Willowbrook B45F	Todmorden Joint Omnibus Committee	9	R
THL 261H	1970	Bristol RELL6G	ECW B53F	West Riding Automobile Co	261	RP
MCK 229J	1971	Leyland Panther PSUR1B/1R	Pennine B47D	Preston Corporation	229	RP
OWY 750K	1972	Bristol RESL6G	ECW B33D	Keighley-West Yorkshire Services	2109	RP
WEX 685M	1973	AEC Swift 3MP2R	ECW B43D	Great Yarmouth Corporation	85	RP
MUA 865P	1976	Leyland Atlantean AN68/1R	Roe H43/30F	Yorkshire Woollen District Transport Co	768	R

Notes:

DHN 475	Rebodied 1947 with 1938 body
TWY 8	New in 1950 registered JWT 112; rebodied and reregistered in 1958
NHU 2	Prototype Bristol LS
OWY 750K	Originally B44F.
MUA 865P	Rebodied 1981

East Pennine Transport Group

Contact address: 23 George Street, Lindley, Huddersfield HD3 3LY
Affiliation: Transport Trust; Keighley Bus Museum
Brief description: An active group progressing with the restoration of a number of interesting vehicles. Please write to the Huddersfield address if you wish to arrange a visit.

Events planned: Please see enthusiast press for details
Opening days/times: Visits to workshop only; strictly by prior arrangement.

Registration	Date	Chassis	Body	New to	Fleet No	Status
BRM 596	1936	Leyland Titan TD4	ECW L27/28R	Cumberland Motor Services	291	RP
AVH 470+	1938	Karrier E6	Park Royal H36/28R	Huddersfield Corporation	470	A
CCX 777	1945	Daimler CWA6	Duple L27/28R	Huddersfield Joint Omnibus Committee	217	RP
CCX 801	1945	Guy Arab II	Roe L27/26R	County Motors of Lepton	70	RP
FVH 1	1951	Guy Arab UF	Park Royal B43F	Huddersfield Joint Omnibus Committee	1	RP
HVH 234	1954	AEC Regent III 9613E	East Lancs L30/28R	Huddersfield Joint Omnibus Committee	234	RP
8340 U	1958	Leyland Tiger Cub PSUC1/2	Burlingham C41F	Wallace Arnold Tours of Leeds		RP
CBA 966L	1973	Bedford J2SZ2	Plaxton C15F	Salford Social Services		R
+ Trolleybus						

Notes:

BRM 596	Rebodied 1950
CCX 801	Rebodied 1953

Friends of King Alfred Buses

Contact address: 27 White Dirt Lane, Catherington, Waterlooville, Hampshire, PO8 ONB
E-mail: FOKABevents@lineone.net
Brief description: The collection includes 12 former King Alfred Motor Services vehicles that have been rescued from around the world and restored. A charitable trust, FoKAB aims eventually to establish a museum. In the meantime, the vehicles can be viewed at the annual running day and other events.
Events planned: 1 Jan 2003 — Annual running day at Winchester.

Registration	Date	Chassis	Body	New to	Fleet No	Status
OU 9286	1931	Dennis 30cwt	Short B18F	King Alfred Motor Services		R
HOR 493	1949	Leyland Titan PD2/1	Leyland H30/26R	Isle of Man Road Services	72	A
JAA 708	1950	Leyland Olympic HR40	Weymann B40F	King Alfred Motor Services		RP
POU 494	1956	Leyland Titan PD2/24	East Lancs L27/28R	King Alfred Motor Services		R
WCG 104	1959	Leyland Tiger Cub PSUC1/1	Weymann B45F	King Alfred Motor Services		R
326 CAA	1961	Bedford SB3	Harrington C41F	King Alfred Motor Services		R
595 LCG	1964	AEC Renown 3B2RA	Park Royal H43/31F	King Alfred Motor Services		R
596 LCG	1964	AEC Renown 3B2RA	Park Royal H43/31F	King Alfred Motor Services		R
CCG 704C	1965	Bedford VAL 14	Plaxton C49F	King Alfred Motor Services		R
HOR 590E	1967	Leyland Atlantean PDR1/2	Roe O43/31F	King Alfred Motor Services		R
HOR 592E	1967	Leyland Atlantean PDR1/2	Roe H43/33F	King Alfred Motor Services		R
UOU 417H	1970	Leyland Panther PSUR1A/1R	Plaxton B52F	King Alfred Motor Services		RP
UOU 419H	1970	Leyland Panther PSUR1A/1R	Plaxton B52F	King Alfred Motor Services		R

Notes:

HOR 493	To be restored as King Alfred vehicle; originally registered KMN 502
POU 494	Repatriated from the USA in 1993
595 LCG	On loan from the Oxford Bus Museum
596 LCG	Repatriated from the USA in 1988
CCG 704C	Restoration involved body-swap.
HOR 590E	Originally H43/33F; acquired by Bristol Omnibus Co (8602) and converted to open-top in 1979
HOR 592E	Acquired by Bristol Omnibus Co (8600) and converted to open-top in 1979; restored using roof from sister vehicle HOR591E

Left: **The Friends of King Alfred Buses are the custodians of both of the company's 1964 Park Royalbodied AEC Renowns. 596 LCG is restored in earlier livery.**
Philip Lamb

Glasgow Bus Museum

Contact address: Bridgeton Bus Garage, 76 Fordneuk Street, Glasgow G40 3AH
Phobe: 0141 554 0544
Web site: www.glasgowbusmuseum.co.uk
Affiliation: NARTM, SVVF
Brief description: Established in a former Glasgow Corporation bus depot, the collection has a distinctly west of Scotland bias. However, the museum also houses examples from other areas of the UK and Eire.

Opening days/times: To be confirmed. Telephone for access information.
Directions by car: From City centre follow London Road eastbound.
Directions by public transport: First Glasgow 18 and 64 from City centre. SPT rail network to Bridgeton station
Events planned: 24/25 August 2002 — Open Weekend
Facilities: B(e), D, T

Registration	Date	Chassis	Body	New to	Fleet No	Status
BUS 181	1938	AEC Regent O661	Scottish Commercial	Glasgow Corporation	615	R
HUS 675	1950	Albion Victor FT21N	Bennett B20F	Glasgow Education Department		A
HUS 676	1950	Albion Victor FT21N	no body -	Glasgow Education Department		A
MSU 252	1956	Ford 502E	Harrington B20F	Bristol Aircraft at Filton		R
FYS 996+	1958	BUT RETB1	Burlingham B50F	Glasgow Corporation	TBS21	A
FYS 999	1958	Daimler CVD6-30	Alexander H41/32R	Glasgow Corporation	D217	R
SGD 65	1958	Leyland Titan PD2/24	Alexander H33/28R	Glasgow Corporation	L163	R
SGD 239	1959	Daimler CVD6	Alexander H33/28R	Glasgow Corporation	D256	A
SGD 241	1959	Daimler CVD6	Alexander H33/28R	Glasgow Corporation	D258	A
OMS 244	1960	Albion Nimbus NS3L	Alexander C31F	Midland Bluebird		A
SGD 491	1960	AEC Regent V 2D2RA	Alexander H41/31F	Glasgow Corporation	A341	A
603 CYS	1961	Bedford C5C1	Duple C29F	David MacBrayne of Glasgow	179	R
SGD 448	1961	Leyland Titan PD3/2	Alexander H41/31F	Glasgow Corporation	L446	R
SGD 500	1961	AEC Regent V 2D2RA	Alexander H41/31F	Glasgow Corporation	A350	RP

The recently established Glasgow Bus Museum is host to that city's former D217, a 1958 Alexander-bodied Daimler CVD6. *Martin Denman*

Registration	Date	Chassis	Body	New to	Fleet No	Status
WLT 759	1961	AEC Routemaster R2RH	Park Royal H36/28R	London Transport	RM 759	R
828 SHW	1964	Bristol Lodekka FLF6B	ECW H38/32F	Bristol Omnibus Co		R
DBA 227C	1965	Leyland Atlantean PDR1/1	MCW O43/33F	Salford City Transport	227	A
BJK 674D	1966	Leyland Titan PD2A/30	East Lancs H32/28R	Eastbourne Corporation	74	RP
HGA 983D	1966	Bedford VAS 1	Willowbrook B24FM	David MacBrayne of Glasgow	210	R
MGB 286E	1967	Bedford SB5	Plaxton C41F	David MacBrayne of Glasgow	168	R
VML 5G	1968	Leyland Atlantean PDR2/1	Park Royal H47/32F	Road Transport Training Board		A
XGA 8J	1970	Leyland Atlantean PDR1A/1	Alexander H45/29F	Glasgow Corporation	LA510	A
HGD 894L	1973	Leyland Atlantean AN68/1R	Alexander H45/29F	Glasgow Corporation	LA688	A
GGG 300N	1974	Volvo Ailsa AB57	Alexander H44/35F	Greater Glasgow PTE	AV1	RP
SCS 335M	1974	Leyland Leopard PSU3/3R	Alexander DP49F	Western SMT Co	L466	R
KRH 411P	1975	Scania Metropolitan BR111DH	Metro Cammell H44/29F	Kingston upon Hull		A
MGE 183P	1975	Ailsa B55-10	Alexander H44/35F	Glasgow Corporation	AV8	A
MIL 7618	1975	Leyland National	Leyland National B50F	West Midlands PTE		A
CWG 720V	1979	Leyland Atlantean AN68A/1R	Alexander H45/29D	South Yorkshire PTE		RP
FSU 102T	1979	Leyland Atlantean AN68A/1R	Alexander H45/33F	Greater Glasgow PTE	LA1285	A
GGE 156T	1979	Leyland National 10351A/1R	Leyland National B41F	Greater Glasgow PTE	LN1	A
HRS 265V	1979	Leyland Atlantean AN68A/1R	Alexander O45/29D	Grampian Regional Transport	265	R
HSD 76V	1979	Leyland Fleetline FE30AGR	Alexander H44/31F	Western SMT Co		A
WDS 115V	1979	Leyland Fleetline FE30AGR	Alexander H44/31F	Western SMT Co		A
WTS 270T	1979	Volvo Ailsa B55-10	Alexander H44/31D	Tayside Regional Council		RP
CUS 302X	1980	Leyland Atlantean AN68A/1R	Alexander H45/33F	Strathclyde Transport	LA1448	R
LHS 748V	1980	Volvo Ailsa B55-10	Alexander H44/35F	Central SMT Co		RP
RDS 597W	1980	Leyland Atlantean AN68A/1R	Alexander H45/33F	Greater Glasgow PTE	LA1408	A
CUS 297X	1981	Leyland Atlantean AN68A/1R	Alexander H45/33F	Strathclyde Transport	LA1442	A
UGB 193W	1981	Leyland Atlantean AN68A/1R	Alexander H45/33F	Strathclyde Transport	LA1440	RP
UGB 196W	1981	Leyland Atlantean AN68A/1R	Alexander H45/33F	Strathclyde Transport	LA1443	A
70 JZL	1982	Bombardier GM DD	Bombardier H45/27F	Dublin Bus		RP
ULS 640X	1982	MCW Metrobus DR104/10	Alexander H45/33F	Midland Scottish		RP
XMS 422Y	1983	Leyland Leopard	Alexander B49F	Midland Scottish	MFE22	RP
+Trolleybus						

Notes:

BUS 181   Converted to Breakdown Vehicle by J Hunter A1 buses

Golcar Transport Collection

Contact address: 45 Cowlersley Lane, Cowlersley, Huddersfield HD4 5TZ

Brief description: A unique collection of Karrier vehicles, most of which are long-term restoration projects. The collection includes two WL6 six-wheeled saloons.

Opening days/times: Collection opens to coincide with craft weekends at the Colne Valley Museum; can be opened at other times by prior arrangement.

Registration	Date	Chassis	Body	New to	Fleet No	Status
note v	1922	Karrier	(unknown) B20F	(unknown)		A
WT 9156	1925	Karrier JH	Strachan & Brown B26F	Premier Transport of Keighley		RP
DY 5029	1928	Karrier JKL	London Lorries C26D	A Timpson & Son of Catford	117	A
KD 3185	1928	Karrier WL6	Liverpool Corporation B38R	Liverpool Corporation		A
TE 5780	1928	Karrier WL6	English Electric B32F	Ashton under Lyne Corporation	8	RP
VH 2088	1929	Karrier ZA	(unknown) B14F			RP
RB 4757	1932	Commer Centaur	Reeve & Kenning B14D	H G Fox of Alfreton		RP
JC 5313	1938	Guy Wolf	Waveney C20F	Llandudno UDC		R
14 PKR	1961	Karrier BFD	Plaxton C14F	W Davis & Sons of Sevenoaks		A

Notes:

note v   Unregistered solid-tyred disc-wheeled chassis.

WT 9156   Body originally on EH 4960

VH 2088   Period body acquired from Anglesey

RB 4757   Carries 1929 body from Ford AA chassis

Many former Llandudno buses survive in preservation, including Waveney-bodied Guy Wolf JC 5313, part of the Golcar Transport Collection. *Philip Lamb*

Huddersfield Passenger Transport Group

Contact address: 20 Alma Drive, Dalton, Huddersfield HD5 9EF
Brief description: The collection is based in Huddersfield and comprises nearly 20 vehicles, including commercial vehicles and trams.

There are currently six buses in the collection.
Opening days/times: Please contact the above address for an appointment to view.

Registration	Date	Chassis	Body	New to	Fleet No	Status
RWU 534R	1977	Leyland Leopard	Plaxton	Halifax Corporation	8534	R
ECX 425	1949	AEC Regent III 9612E	Northern Coach Builders L29/26R	Huddersfield Joint Omnibus Committee	225	RP
EFV 300	1951	Leyland Titan PD2/5	Burlingham FH29/23C	Blackpool Corporation	300	RP
ODE 182	1952	Sentinel STC6	Sentinel B44F	Edwards Bros of Crymych		RP
HVH 472D	1966	Daimler CVG6LX-30	East Lancs H41/29F	Huddersfield Corporation	472	R
JWU 244N	1975	Leyland Leopard PSU4C/4R	Plaxton B43F	West Yorkshire PTE	8501	RP

Notes:
JWU 244N   Owned by the National Coalmining Museum at Wakefield

Kelvin Amos Collection

Contact address: 30 Blandford Close, Nailsea, Bristol BS48 2QQ

Brief description: The two vehicles in the collection are regularly shown and run on free bus services.

Registration	Date	Chassis	Body	New to	Fleet No	Status
LHT 911	1948	Bristol L5G	Brislington Body Works B35R	Bristol Tramways	2388	R
KED 546F	1968	Leyland Panther Cub PSURC1	East Lancs B41D	Warrington Corporation	92	R

Notes:

LHT 911	Rebodied 1958 with 1950 body

Lancastrian Transport Trust

Contact address: 1 Beverley Grove, South Shore, Blackpool, Lancashire FY4 2BG

E-mail: philip@ltt.org.uk

Web site: www.ltt.org.uk

Brief description: The Trust is dedicated to preserving historic buses from Lancashire. Vehicles can often be seen at local rallies and other events.

Membership details: Support organisation is TransSupport with a £10 annual membership fee. Quarterly magazine published *In Trust*.

Registration	Date	Chassis	Body	New to	Fleet No	Status
CCK 663	1949	Leyland Titan PD2/3	Brush L27/26R	Ribble Motor Services	2687	A
DFV 146	1949	Leyland Titan PD2/5	Burlingham FH31/23C	Blackpool Corporation	246	A
760 CTD	1957	Leyland Titan PD2/20	Northern Counties H30/28R	Lytham St Annes Corporation	61	A
561 TD	1962	Daimler Fleetline CRG6LX	Northern Counties H43/33F	Lancashire United Transport	97	R
RRN 405	1962	Leyland Atlantean PDR1/1	Weymann L38/33F	Ribble Motor Services	1805	R
YFR 351	1962	Leyland Titan PD3/1	Metro Cammell FH41/32R	Blackpool Corporation	351	A

This early lowbridge Leyland Atlantean/Weymann is part of the Lancastrian Transport Trust's collection of vehicles from the Fylde area. *Philip Lamb*

Registration	Date	Chassis	Body	New to	Fleet No	Status
CTF 627B	1964	Leyland Titan PD2A/27	Massey H37/27F	Lytham St Annes Corporation	70	R
HFR 512E	1967	Leyland Titan PD3A/1	MCW H41/30R	Blackpool Corporation	512	R
HFR 515E	1967	Leyland Titan PD3A/1	MCW H41/30R	Blackpool Corporation	515	A
LFR 540G	1968	Leyland Titan PD3/11	MCW H41/30R	Blackpool Corporation	540	A
PFR 554H	1970	AEC Swift MP2R	Marshall B47D	Blackpool Corporation	554	R
ATD 281J	1971	Leyland Atlantean PDR1A/1	Northern Counties H44/33F	Lytham St Annes Corporation	77	R
RTJ 422L	1972	Daimler Fleetline CRG6LXB-33	Northern Counties H47/32F	Lancashire United Transport	394	A
STJ 847L	1972	Seddon RU	Pennine B51F	Lytham St Annes Corporation	47	A

Notes:
CTF 627B   On loan from St Helens Transport Museum

Legionnaire Group

Contact address: 66 Montfort Road, Strood, Rochester, Kent
ME2 3EX
E-mail: bob.wingrove@btinternet.com

Brief description: The group aims to restore at least one of each combination of chassis/Legionnaire so that Harrington's last body style is represented in preservation.

Registration	Date	Chassis	Body	New to	Fleet No	Status
72 MMJ	1964	Bedford VAL 14	Harrington C52F	Reliance Coaches of Meppershall	72	RP
CDK 409C	1965	Bedford VAL 14	Harrington C52F	Yelloway Motor Services of Rochdale		A
JNK 681C	1965	Ford Thames 36 676E	Harrington C52F	SP Coaches of Sutton		RP

Notes:
JNK 681C   Used as Harrington demonstrator when new

Meltham Mills Bus Museum

Contact address: 1 Vicar Park Road, Norton Tower, Halifax
HX2 0NL
Brief description: A collection of privately-owned vehicles most of which operated originally in West Yorkshire.

Events planned: Please see enthusiast press for details.
Opening days/times: The collection is not normally open to the public, but an appointment to view can be arranged by contacting the above address.

Registration	Date	Chassis	Body	New to	Fleet No	Status
JUB 29	1932	Leyland Titan TD2	Eastern Counties L27/26R	Keighley-West Yorkshire Services	K451	A
JX 7046	1939	AEC Regent O661	Park Royal H30/26R	Halifax Corporation	80	A
AJX 369	1946	AEC Regent III 9612E	Park Royal H33/26R	Halifax Joint Omnibus Committee	243	A
JX 9106	1946	AEC Regal O662	Weymann	Hebble Motor Services	181	A
HHP 755	1948	Maudslay Regal III	Duple FC33F	Greenslades Tours of Exeter		A
JXN 370	1949	Leyland Titan 7RT	Park Royal H30/26RD	London Transport	RTL 47	A
BCP 671	1950	AEC Regent III 9612E	Park Royal H33/26R	Halifax Joint Omnibus Committee	277	R
LTF 254	1950	AEC Regent III 9612E	Park Royal H33/26R	Morecambe & Heysham Corporation	69	R
ROD 765	1958	AEC Regent V MD3RV	Metro Cammell H33/26RD	Devon General	DR 765	R
3916 UB	1959	AEC Regent V 2D3RA	Metro Cammell H38/32R	Leeds City Transport	916	R
LJX 198	1959	AEC Regent V 2D3RA	Metro Cammell H39/32F	Hebble Motor Services	307	R
LJX 215	1960	AEC Regent V 2D3RA	Metro Cammell H40/32F	Halifax Joint Omnibus Committee	215	RP

Notes:
JUB 29	Rebodied in 1951 using 1932 body
JX 9106	Converted to tow lorry in 1956 and renumbered L4
HHP 755	Exhibited at the 1948 Commercial Motor Show
JXN 370	Originally H30/26R

Merseyside Transport Trust

Contact address: 88 Hawthorne Road, Bootle, Merseyside,
L20 9JX
E-mail: rob@aquaventurers.co.uk

Affiliation: NARTM; AEC Society; Leyland Society
Brief description: A collection of around 35 vehicles, mostly from the Merseyside area but including others of special interest.

Registration	Date	Chassis	Body	New to	Fleet No	Status
GKD 434	1946	AEC Regent II O661	Weymann/LCPT H30/26R	Liverpool Corporation	A233	A
HKF 820	1949	AEC Regent III 9612E	Weymann/LCPT H30/26R	Liverpool Corporation	A344	RP
JKC 178	1949	Daimler CVA6	Northern Counties H30/26R	Liverpool Corporation	D553	A
KMN 519	1950	Leyland Comet CP01	Park Royal B30F	Douglas Corporation	21	R
LFM 756	1951	Bristol LL6B	ECW B39R	Crosville Motor Services	SLB175	R
MMN 302	1951	Leyland Olympic HR40	Weymann B40F	Isle of Man Road Services	84	R
NMN 907	1951	Leyland Royal Tiger PSU1/13	Leyland B44F	Isle of Man Road Services	89	A
MKB 994	1952	AEC Regent III 9613A	Crossley H30/26R	Liverpool Corporation	A801	A
NKD 536	1953	AEC Regent III 9613S	Crossley H30/26R	Liverpool Corporation	A36	RP
NKD 540	1954	AEC Regent III 9613S	Saunders Roe H32/26R	Liverpool Corporation	A40	RP
RKC 262	1955	Leyland Titan PD2/20	Alexander H32/26R	Liverpool Corporation	L161	RP
SKB 168	1956	Leyland Royal Tiger PSU1/13	Crossley/MCW HDC23/21F	Liverpool Corporation	XL171	RP
SKB 224	1956	Leyland Titan PD2/20	Crossley/LCPT H32/26R	Liverpool Corporation	L227	RP
VKB 711	1956	Leyland Titan PD2/20	Crossley H33/29R	Liverpool Corporation	L255	RP
VKB 841	1957	Leyland Titan PD2/20	Crossley H33/29R	Liverpool Corporation	L320	A
VKB 900	1957	AEC Regent V D3RV	Metro Cammell H33/29R	Liverpool Corporation	A267	R
116 TMD	1958	AEC Bridgemaster B3RA	Park Royal H43/33R	Liverpool Corporation	E3	A
371 BKA	1959	AEC Regent V LD3RA	Park Royal FH40/32F	Liverpool Corporation	E1	R
372 BKA	1959	Leyland Atlantean PDR1/1	Metro Cammell H43/35F	Liverpool Corporation	E2	RP
256 SFM	1961	Bristol Lodekka FLF6B	ECW H38/22F	Crosville Motor Services	DFB43	A
875 VFM	1961	Bristol Lodekka FSF6G	ECW H34/26F	Crosville Motor Services	DFG65	RP
891 VFM	1961	Bristol Lodekka FSF6G	ECW O34/26F	Crosville Motor Services	DFG81	RP
501 KD	1962	Leyland Atlantean PDR1/1	Metro Cammell H43/35F	Liverpool Corporation	L501	R
GFM 180C	1965	Bristol Lodekka FS6B	ECW H33/27RD	Crosville Motor Services	DFB180	RP
FKF 801D	1966	Leyland Atlantean PDR1/1	MCW H43/35F	Liverpool City Transport	L801	A
FKF 835E	1967	Leyland Atlantean PDR1/1	MCW H43/28D	Liverpool City Transport	L835	RP
FKF 933G	1968	Leyland Panther PSUR1A/1R	MCW B47D	Liverpool City Transport	1054	RP
SKB 695G	1969	Bristol RELL6G	Park Royal B45D	Liverpool City Transport	2025	RP
UKA 562H	1969	Leyland Atlantean PDR2/1	Alexander H47/32D	Liverpool City Transport	1111	R
XKC 862K	1971	Leyland Atlantean PDR2/1	Alexander H49/31D	Merseyside PTE	1235	R
BKC 236K	1972	Leyland Atlantean PDR1A/1	Alexander H43/32F	Merseyside PTE	1236	R

Notes:

KMN 519	On loan to British Commercial Vehicle Museum at Leyland
SKB 168	Originally B40D numbered SL171; rebuilt by Metro Cammell in 1961
116 TMD	Former AEC demonstrator; acquired by Liverpool Corporation (E3) in 1959
891 VFM	Originally H34/26F
FKF 835E	Originally H43/35F. Rebuilt by Pennine Coachcraft 1969.

The Mike Sutcliffe Collection

Phone: Phone: 01525 221676
Affiliation: NARTM; Leyland Society member
Brief description: A collection of 20 vehicles, mainly buses of Leyland manufacture from the period 1908 to 1934, this is the most significant collection of of early motorbuses in the world, and includes the oldest British-built motorbus.

Opening days/times: Viewing can be arranged by prior appointment only. There is no charge, but donations are welcome.

Registration	Date	Chassis	Body	New to	Fleet No	Status
LN 7270	1908	Leyland X2	Thomas Tilling O18/16RO	London Central Motor Omnibus Co	14	R
HE 12	1913	Leyland S3.30.T	Brush B27F	Barnsley & District Electric Traction Co	5	RP
LF 9967	1913	Leyland S3.30.T	Birch O20/16RO	Wellingborough Motor Omnibus Co	H	R
CC 1087	1914	Leyland S4.36.T3	Leyland Ch32	London & North Western Railway	59	R
BD 209	1921	Leyland G7	Dodson Ch/B32D	United Counties Omnibus Co	B15	R
C 2367	1921	Leyland G	Phoenix O23/20RO	Todmorden Corporation	14	R
DM 2583	1923	Leyland SG7	Leyland FB40D	Brookes Bros ('White Rose') of Rhyl	27	R
XU 7498	1924	Leyland LB5	Dodson O26/22RO	Chocolate Express Omnibus Co	B6	R
BT 8939	1925	Leyland C7	Barnaby B26R	Lee & Beaulah of Elloughton	17	RP
PW 8605	1926	ADC 415	United B35F	United Automobile Services	E61	A
CK 4518	1931	Leyland Lion LT2	Leyland B30F	Ribble Motor Services	1161	A
YG 7831	1934	Leyland Tiger TS6	Northern Counties B36R	Todmorden Joint Omnibus Committee	15	A

Notes:

LN 7270	Body new 1906 Bought by LGOC 1908. Orig on Milnes Daimler
LF 9967	On loan to British Commercial Vehicle Museum at Leyland
CC 1087	Re-registered XA8086 in 1919; reverted to CC1087 in 1980
C 2367	On loan to Manchester Museum of Transport
BD 209	Formerly a Dodson demonstrator.
YG 7831	Rebuilt to recovery vehicle; to be restored as bus

This Leyland with 'Torpedo' Charabanc body lasted for only a few months in service with the London North Western Railway before being requisitioned for war use in 1914. *Mike Sutcliffe*

North East Bus Preservation Society

Contact address: 'Relly Steading', Broom Park, Durham DH7 7RJ
Phone: 0191 384 5146
E-mail: r.l.keil@Durham.ac.uk
Affiliation: NARTM
Brief description: The collection is displayed at an 1820 former

locomotive shed on the Bowes Railway. This accommodates up to 10 vehicles, and so vehicles rotate between this and other locations. If you wish to view a particular vehicle, you will need to mention this when making arrangements to view.

Opening days/times: Viewing by prior arrangement only.

Registration	Date	Chassis	Body	New to	Fleet No	Status
CN 4740	1931	SOS IM4	Short B34F	Northern General Transport Co	540	A
BTN 113	1934	Daimler COS4	Northern Coach Builders B34R	Newcastle Corporation	173	A
CN 6100	1934	Northern General Transport SE6 (LSE4)	Short B44F	Northern General Transport Co	604	RP
DPT 848	1939	Leyland Tiger TS8	Roe B32F	Sunderland District	159	R
EF 7380	1942	Leyland Titan TD7	Roe H26/22C	West Hartlepool Corporation	36	R
HHN 202	1947	Bristol L5G	ECW B35R	Bells of Westerhope		R
HUP 236	1948	Albion Valiant CX39N	ACB C33F	Economic Bus Services of Whitburn	W7	R
JPT 544	1948	Daimler CVD6	Willowbrook B35F	Venture Transport Co of Consett	156	R
LVK 123	1948	Leyland Titan PD2/1	Leyland H30/26R	Newcastle Corporation	123	RP
ABR 433	1949	Crossley DD42/7C	Crossley H56R	Sunderland Corporation	100	RP
CFK 340	1949	AEC Regal III 6821A	Burlingham C33F	H & E Burnham of Worcester		R
LPT 328	1950	AEC Regal III 9621E	Burlingham C33F	Gillet Bros of Quarrington Hill	31	R
NVK 341	1950	AEC Regent III 9613A	Northern Coach Builders H30/26R	Newcastle Corporation	341	R
CBR 539	1952	Guy Arab III	Roe H33/25R	Sunderland Corporation	139	RP
PHN 699	1952	Guy Arab III	Roe B41C	Darlington Corporation	26	RP
SHN 301	1952	AEC Regal IV 9821E	Burlingham C41C	Scotts Greys of Darlington	5	R
DCN 83	1953	AEC Beadle	Beadle C35F	Northern General Transport Co	1483	A
SPT 65	1955	Guy Arab LUF	Weymann B44F	Northern General Transport Co	1665	RP
TUP 859	1956	AEC Regent V MD3RV	Roe H35/28R	Hartlepool Corporation	4	RP
UFJ 292	1957	Guy Arab IV	Massey H30/26R	Exeter Corporation	52	R

Registration	Date	Chassis	Body	New to	Fleet No	Status
VUP 328	1957	Leyland Tiger Cub PSUC1/1	Crossley B44F	Economic Bus Services of Whitburn	A2	A
AFT 930	1958	Leyland Titan PD3/4	Metro Cammell H41/32R	Tynemouth & District	230	RP
MJD 759	1958	AEC Reliance MU3RV	Roe C41C	Essex County Coaches of Stratford		R
YPT 796	1958	AEC Reliance MU3RV	Roe C41C	Economic Bus Services of Whitburn	W3	R
221 JVK	1962	Leyland Atlantean PDR1/1	Alexander H44/34F	Newcastle Corporation	221	RP
WNL 259A	1962	AEC Reliance 4MU3R	Plaxton B55F	Economic Bus Services of Whitburn	W5	R
6249 UP	1963	Leyland Leopard PSU3/3RT	Alexander DP51F	Venture Transport Co of Consett	249	R
ACU 304B	1963	Leyland Leopard PSU3/3R	Plaxton B55F	Stanhope Motor Services		R
EUP 405B	1964	AEC Routemaster 3R2RH	Park Royal H41/31F	Northern General Transport Co	2105	R
PCN 762	1964	AEC Routemaster 3R2RH	Park Royal H41/31F	Northern General Transport Co	2099	R
WBR 248	1964	Atkinson Alpha PM746HL	Marshall B45D	Sunderland Corporation	48	R
FBR 53D	1966	Leyland Panther PSUR1/1R	Strachan B47D	Sunderland Corporation	53	R
ECU 201E	1967	Bristol RESL6L	ECW B45D	South Shields Corporation	1	R
WHN 411G	1969	Bristol VRTSL6LX	ECW H39/31F	United Automobile Services	601	A
PCW 203J	1971	Bristol RESL6L	Pennine B45F	Burnley Colne & Nelson	103	R
MCN 30K	1972	Leyland/NGT Tynesider	Weymann/Northern General H39/29F	Northern General Transport Co	3000	R
GGR 103N	1974	Leyland Atlantean AN68/2R	Northern Counties H47/36F	OK Motor Services		RP
GUP 907N	1975	Bristol LH6L	ECW B43F	United Automobile Services	1623	R
TUP 329R	1976	Bristol VRTSL3/501	ECW H43/31F	Northern General Transport Co	3329	RP
VPT 598R	1977	Leyland National 11351A/1R	Leyland National B49F	Northern General Transport Co	4598	RP
RCU 838S	1978	Leyland Fleetline FE30AGR	Alexander H44/30F	Tyne & Wear PTE	838	R
UTN 501Y	1983	MCW Metrobus DR102/31	MCW H46/31F	Northern General Transport Co	3501	R

Notes:

HHN 202	Rebodied 1957 with 1946 body; passed to Durham District Services (DB216) in 1959
ABR 433	Fitted with Gardner 5LW engine
WNL 259A	Originally registered 8031PT
ACU 304B	Originally registered 6MPT
PCN 762	Originally registered RCN699
MCN 30K	Rebuilt from 1958 Leyland Titan PD3/4 new to Tyneside Tramways & Tramroads Co (49) registered NNL 49
RCU 838S	Originally H44/27D

Left: **The North East Bus Preservation Society collection includes this Massey-bodied Guy Arab IV, new to Exeter, but preserved in the livery of latter day operator, Shaw Brothers of Spennymoor.** *David Reed*

Below: **Sunderland District 159 is a Roe-bodied Leyland TS8 saloon.** *David Reed*

Peter Stanier Collection

Phone: 01474 814476
Brief description: A collection of preserved Leyland petrol-engined vehicles with their origins in the island of Jersey

Opening days/times: Not normally open for viewing. Arrangements to visit can be made, strictly by appointment, telephoning first for details

Registration	Date	Chassis	Body	New to	Fleet No	Status
DM 6228	1929	Leyland Lioness LTB1	Leyland C26D	Brooks Bros of Rhyl	7	R
SV 6107	1931	Leyland Titan TD1	Leyland L24/24R	Jersey Motor Transport Co	24	R

Notes:
SV 6107   1931 body fitted 1934. Chassis new to Jersey, originally registered J 1199

Ribble Vehicle Preservation Trust

Contact address: 6 Crompton Road, Lostock, Bolton BL6 4LP
Brief description: The Trust promotes the preservation and restoration of vehicles from Ribble and associated companies.

Registration	Date	Chassis	Body	New to	Fleet No	Status
RN 7588	1935	Leyland Tiger TS7	Burlingham B35F	Ribble Motor Services	209	R
ACK 796	1944	Guy Arab II	Northern Counties / Bond UL27/26R	Ribble Motor Services	2413	A
ACB 904	1947	Guy Arab II	Northern Counties	Blackburn Corporation	502	A
CRG 811	1947	Daimler CVD6	Alexander C35F	Aberdeen Corporation	11	A
CCK 359	1948	Leyland Titan PD2/3	Leyland L27/26R	Ribble Motor Services	2584	A
CRS 834	1948	Daimler CVD6	Walker/Aberdeen CT C31F	Aberdeen Corporation	44	A
DRN 289	1950	Leyland Titan PD2/3	Leyland L27/26RD	Ribble Motor Services	1349	A
MTC 540	1950	AEC Regent III 9613E	Park Royal H30/26R	Morecambe & Heysham Corporation	72	RP
ERN 700	1952	Leyland Royal Tiger PSU1/13	Leyland B44F	Ribble Motor Services	377	A
FCK 844	1954	Leyland Tiger Cub PSUC1/1	Saunders Roe B44F	Ribble Motor Services	412	R
FCK 884	1954	Leyland Tiger Cub PSUC1/1T	Saunders Roe B44F	Ribble Motor Services	452	R
HRN 31	1955	Leyland Titan PD2/13	Metro Cammell H33/28RD	Ribble Motor Services	1391	A
HRN 39	1955	Leyland Titan PD2/13	Metro Cammell H33/28RD	Ribble Motor Services	1399	A
JCK 530	1956	Leyland Titan PD2/12	Burlingham H33/28RD	Ribble Motor Services	1455	R
JCK 542	1956	Leyland Titan PD2/12	Burlingham H33/28RD	Ribble Motor Services	1467	RP
JRN 41	1956	Leyland Tiger Cub PSUC1/2T	Burlingham C41F	Ribble Motor Services	975	A
528 CTF	1957	Leyland Titan PD2/40	Weymann L29/28RD	J Fishwick & Sons of Leyland	5	R
881 BTF	1958	Leyland Titan PD2/41	East Lancs H35/28R	Lancaster City Transport	881	A
KCK 869	1958	Leyland Titan PD3/4	Burlingham FH41/31F	Ribble Motor Services	1523	A
KCK 914	1958	Leyland Titan PD3/4	Burlingham FH41/31F	Ribble Motor Services	1553	A
NRN 586	1960	Leyland Atlantean PDR1/1	Metro Cammell H44/33F	Ribble Motor Services	1686	R
SFV 421	1960	Leyland Atlantean PDR1/1	Weymann CH34/16Ft	W C Standerwick	25	A
PRN 145	1961	Leyland Atlantean PDR1/1	Metro Cammell H44/33F	Scout Motor Services of Preston	5	RP
PRN 906	1961	Leyland Titan PD3/4	Metro Cammell H39/31F	Preston Corporation	14	RP
RRN 428	1962	Leyland Atlantean PDR1/1	Weymann CH39/20F	Ribble Motor Services	1279	R
TCK 465	1963	Leyland Leopard PSU3/1R	Marshall B53F	Ribble Motor Services	465	RP
TCK 726	1963	Leyland Leopard PSU3/3RT	Harrington C49F	Ribble Motor Services	726	RP
ARN 811C	1965	Leyland Leopard PSU3/3RT	Weymann DP49F	Ribble Motor Services	811	RP
FPT 6G	1969	Leyland Leopard PSU3/3RT	Plaxton C51F	Weardale Motor Services of Frosterley		A
HRN 249G	1969	Bristol RELL6G	ECW B41D	Ribble Motor Services	249	RP
LRN 321J	1970	Bristol RESL6L	Marshall B47F	Ribble Motor Services	321	A
NCK 338J	1971	Bristol RESL6L	ECW B47F	Ribble Motor Services	338	RP
PRN 79K	1972	Bristol VRLLH6L	ECW CH42/18Ct	W C Standerwick	S79	A

Registration	Date	Chassis	Body	New to	Fleet No	Status
PTF 746L	1973	Leyland National 1151/2R	Leyland National B48D	Ribble Motor Services	400	R
UTF 732M	1974	Leyland Leopard PSU3B/4R	Duple C49F	Ribble Motor Services	1052	A
MFR 306P	1976	Leyland Leopard PSU3C/2R	Alexander B53F	Lancaster City Transport	306	R
NNC 855P	1976	AEC Reliance 6U3ZR	Duple C49F	Yelloway Motor Services of Rochdale		R
XCW 955R	1978	Leyland National 11351A/1R	Leyland National B49F	J Fishwick & Sons of Leyland	24	RP
TRN 481V	1979	Leyland Atlantean AN68A/1R	ECW H43/31F	Ribble Motor Services	1481	R
TRN 810V	1979	Leyland National 10351B/1R	Leyland National B44F	Ribble Motor Services	810	RP

Notes:

RN 7588	Rebodied 1949
CRG 811	Rebodied 1958
ACB 904	Breakdown Vehicle
CRS 834	Body rebuilt 1962
ERN 700	Originally B44F
SFV 421	Gay Hostess double deck motorway coach

Ribble 2700, RN 7588, originally number 209, now in the care of the Ribble Vehicle Preservation Group is a 1935 Leyland TS7. Rebodied by Burlingham in 1949. *Philip Lamb*

Rotherham Trolleybus Group

Contact address: 113 Tinker Lane, Walkley, Sheffield S6 5EA
Phone: 0114 266 3173
Affiliation: Sandtoft Transport Centre
Brief description: This group is open to all with an interest in Rotherham area trolleys, the vehicles and the system. Active restoration of the vehicles takes place and the group works closely with Sandtoft Transport Centre. A video *Remember the Trackless* is sold to raise funds for restoration. Vehicles can be viewed by contacting the group.

Registration	Date	Chassis	Body	New to	Fleet No	Status
CET 613+	1942	Sunbeam MS2c	East Lancs B39C	Rotherham Corporation	88	RP
FET 617+	1950	Daimler CTE6	Roe H40/30R	Rotherham Corporation	37	RP
+trolleybus						

Notes:
FET 617   Rebodied 1956 (formerly single-decker)

RTW Bus Group

Contact address: 7 Oldbury Close, St Mary Cray BR5 3TH
Affiliation: RT/RF Register, Cobham Bus Museum, HCVS
Brief description: The group was formed in 1999 and comprises the owners of the preserved RTW vegicles and those interested in the type. The vehicles appear at rallies from time to time. A video on the history of the RTW is available from the group.

Registration	Date	Chassis	Body	New to	Fleet No	Status
KGK 529	1949	Leyland Titan 6RT	Leyland H30/26R	London Transport	RTW 29	R
KGK 575	1949	Leyland Titan 6RT	Leyland H30/26R	London Transport	RTW 75	RP
KLB 908	1949	Leyland Titan 6RT	Leyland H30/26RD	London Transport	RTW 178	R
KLB 915	1949	Leyland Titan 6RT	Leyland H30/26R	London Transport	RTW 185	R
LLU 957	1950	Leyland Titan 6RT	Leyland H30/26R	London Transport	RTW 467	R
LLU 987	1950	Leyland Titan 6RT	Leyland H30/26R	London Transport	RTW 497	R

Note:
KLB 908   Originally H30/26R. Acquired by Stevensons of Spath in 1966 and fitted with platform doors and saloon heaters

London Transport RTW178 is preserved in the livery of subsequent owner Stevensons of Spath, where it operated the 'main road' route to Burton-on-Trent for many years.
Philip Lamb

SELNEC Preservation Society

Contact address: 16 Thurleigh Road, Didsbury, Manchester
M20 2DF
Brief description: A collection of buses from the SELNEC era including SELNEC Standards, the trail-blazing 'Mancunian' and other vehicles from the Greater Manchester area.
Events planned: The operational vehicles will appear at a range of local rallies and shows.

Registration	Date	Chassis	Body	New to	Fleet No	Status
EN 9965	1950	Leyland Titan PD2/4	Weymann	Bury Corporation	165	RP
DNF 708C	1965	Daimler Fleetline CRG6LX	Metro Cammell O43/29C	Manchester Corporation	4708	A
END 832D	1966	Leyland Atlantean PDR1/2	Metro Cammell H43/32F	Manchester Corporation	3832	RP
LNA 166G	1968	Leyland Atlantean PDR2/1	Park Royal H26/7D	Manchester Corporation	1066	R
NNB 547H	1969	Leyland Atlantean PDR2/1	East Lancs H47/32F	Manchester Corporation	1142	A
NNB 589H	1970	Daimler Fleetline CRG6LXB	Park Royal H47/28D	SELNEC PTE	2130	A
ONF 865H	1970	Leyland Atlantean PDR2/1	Park Royal H47/28D	SELNEC PTE	1177	A
PNF 941J	1971	Leyland Atlantean PDR1A/1	Northern Counties H43/32F	SELNEC PTE	EX1	R
RNA 220J	1971	Daimler Fleetline CRG6LXB	Park Royal H47/29D	SELNEC PTE	2220	A
TNB 759K	1972	Daimler Fleetline CRG6LXB	Northern Counties H45/27D	SELNEC PTE	EX19	A
VNB 177L	1972	Daimler Fleetline CRG6LXB	Northern Counties H45/27D	SELNEC PTE	7206	R
VNB 203L	1972	Daimler Fleetline CRG6LXB	Northern Counties H31/4D	SELNEC PTE	7232	R
YDB 453L	1972	Seddon Pennine IV-236	Seddon DP25F	SELNEC PTE	1700	RP
AJA 408L	1973	Bristol VRTSL2/6LXB	ECW H43/32F	SELNEC Cheshire Bus Co	408	RP
WWH 43L	1973	Daimler Fleetline CRG6LXB	Park Royal H43/32F	SELNEC PTE	7185	R
XJA 534L	1973	Leyland Atlantean AN68/1R	Park Royal H43/32F	SELNEC PTE	7143	A
XVU 341M	1973	Seddon Pennine IV-236	Seddon B23F	SELNEC PTE	1711	A
BNE 729N	1974	Seddon Pennine IV-236	Seddon B19F	Greater Manchester PTE	1735	A
BNE 751N	1974	Leyland Atlantean AN68/1R	Northern Counties H43/32F	Greater Manchester PTE	7501	A
BNE 764N	1974	Bristol LH6L	ECW B43F	Greater Manchester PTE	1321	A
XVU 363M	1974	Seddon Pennine IV-236	Seddon B19F	Greater Manchester PTE	1733	A

The SELNEC Preservation Society is dedicated to preserving vehicles from that era of the development of Manchester's public transport system, such as No 6990, a Northern Counties-bodied Leyland Fleetline of 1981. *SELNEC Preservation Society*

Above: '**Mancunian' 1066, a 1968 Leyland PDR2/1/Park Royal passed to SELNEC from Manchester Corporation. It was later converted to an exhibition vehicle, in which condition it is preserved.** *SELNEC Preservation Society*

Below: **Another exhibition vehicle is later SELNEC 'standard' 7232, a 1972 Northern Counties-bodied Daimler Fleetline.** *SELNEC Preservation Society*

Registration	Date	Chassis	Body	New to	Fleet No	Status
HNB 24N	1975	Leyland National 10351/1R	Leyland National B41F	Greater Manchester PTE	105	RP
OBN 502R	1977	Leyland Fleetline FE30GR	Northern Counties H43/32F	Lancashire United Transport	485	A
PTD 640S	1977	Leyland Fleetline FE30GR	Northern Counties H43/32F	Lancashire United Transport	496	A
XBU 1S	1978	Leyland Fleetline FE30GR	Northern Counties H43/32F	Greater Manchester PTE	8001	R
BNC 960T	1979	Leyland Atlantean AN68A/1R	Park Royal H43/32F	Greater Manchester PTE	7960	A
GBU 1V	1979	MCW Metrobus DR101/6	MCW H43/30F	Greater Manchester PTE	5001	RP
GNF 15V	1980	Leyland Titan TNTL11/1RF	Park Royal H47/26F	Greater Manchester PTE	4015	A
GNF 16V	1980	Leyland Fleetline FE30GR	Northern Counties H43/32F	Greater Manchester Transport	8141	RP
NJA 568W	1980	Bristol Olympian B45/TL11/1R	Northern Counties H43/30F	Greater Manchester PTE	1451	RP
DWH 706W	1981	Leyland Fleetline FE30GR	Northern Counties H43/32F	Lancashire United Transport	613	R
SND 460X	1981	Leyland Atlantean AN68B/1R	Northern Counties H43/32F	Greater Manchester Transport	8460	RP
ANA 1Y	1982	Bristol Olympian B45/TL11	Northern Counties H43/30F	Greater Manchester PTE	3001	RP
A765 NNA	1984	Leyland Atlantean AN68D/1R	Northern Counties H43/32F	Greater Manchester PTE	8765	RP
C751 YBA	1985	Dennis Domino SDA 1201	Northern Counties B24F	Greater Manchester PTE	1751	R

Notes:

EN 9965	Converted to Breakdown Vehicle
DNF 708C	Originally H43/32F; awaiting repatriation from USA
LNA 166G	Originally H47/29D; converted by Greater Manchester PTE for use as 'Exhibus' exhibition vehicle - restored in this condition
NNB 589H	Mancunian
ONF 865H	Mancunian
RNA 220J	Mancunian
PNF 941J	Exhibited at 1970 Commercial Motor Show as prototype SELNEC Standard
VNB 203L	Originally H45/27D. Used as exhibition vehice.
VNB 177L	Exhibited at 1972 Commercial Motor Show
OBN 502R	Passed to Greater Manchester PTE (6901) in 1981

PTD 640S	Rebodied 1983. Passed to GMPTE in 1981 as 6912.
XBU 1S	First GMT Leyand Fleetline Standard
BNC 960T	Last Park Royal Bodied Standard
GBU 1V	GM First Metrobus
NJA 568W	Exhibited at 1980 Commercial Motor Show. GM First Olympian
GNF 15V	GM Last Titan
DWH 706W	Passed to Greater Manchester PTE (6990) in 1981. GM Last Fleetline
ANA 1Y	Exhibited at 1982 Commercial Motor Show
A765 NNA	Greater Manchester's last Atlantean
C751 YBA	Exhibited at 1984 Commercial Motor Show

Below: **Dennis Domino/Northern Counties 1751 is the most recent bus preserved by the SELNEC Preservation Society.** *SELNEC Preservation Society*

Southampton & District Transport Heritage Trust

Contact address: 'Paynter', Hook Lane, Hook-by-Warsash, Southampton SO31 9HH
Affiliation: NARTM; WOMP

Brief description: The collection includes a selection of Southampton's fleet from the early 1970s. The small membership carries out restoration work.

Registration	Date	Chassis	Body	New to	Fleet No	Status
FTR 511	1949	Guy Arab III	Park Royal O30/26R	Southampton Corporation	64	R
LOW 271	1954	Guy Arab III	Park Royal H30/26R	Southampton Corporation	71	R
JOW 928	1955	Guy Arab UF	Park Royal B39F	Southampton Corporation	255	A
318 AOW	1962	AEC Regent V 2D3RA	Park Royal H37/29R	Southampton Corporation	318	A
335 AOW	1963	Leyland Titan PD2A/27	Park Royal H37/29R	Southampton Corporation	335	A
BTR 361B	1964	AEC Regent V 2D3RA	Neepsend H37/29R	Southampton Corporation	361	R
BOW 507C	1965	AEC Regent V 2D3RA	East Lancs Neepsend H37/29R	Southampton Corporation	371	R
GTP 175F	1967	Leyland Panther Cub PSURC1	MCW B42D	Portsmouth Corporation	175	R
JOW 499E	1967	AEC Swift MP2R	Strachan B47D	Southampton Corporation	1	A
KOW 910F	1967	AEC Regent V 3D2RA	Neepsend H40/30R	Southampton Corporation	402	A
PCG 888G	1968	AEC Reliance 6U3ZR	Plaxton C55F	Coliseum Coaches of Southampton		A
PCG 889G	1968	AEC Reliance 6MU3R	Plaxton C45F	Coliseum Coaches of Southampton		A
TTA 400H	1970	Bedford SB5	Duple C41F	Otter Coaches of Ottery St Mary		A
BCR 379K	1972	Seddon Pennine RU	Pennine B44F	Southampton Corporation	15	R

Notes:

FTR 511	Converted to Open Top
JOW 928	Originally B36D
BTR 361B	On display at CPPTD Museum Portsmouth.
PCG 888G	Originally C57F

The Southampton & District Heritage Trust has a number of former Southampton buses including Neepsend-bodied AEC Regent V No 361. *Philip Lamb*

Southdown Historic Vehicle Group

Contact address: 73 Cuckfield Crescent, Worthing, West Sussex
E-mail: pd3@btinternet.com
Website: http://home.fastnet.co.uk/gerrycork/worthingbusrally/worthingbusrally.htm
Brief description: A private collection of vehicles most of which operated for Southdown Motor Services or which have south coast connections or have taken our fancy. The collection is not on public view but vehicles are rallied and often appear in service at running days.

Events planned: 28 July 2002 — Worthing Bus Rally & Running Day

Registration	Date	Chassis	Body	New to	Fleet No	Status
EHO 869	1943	Guy Arab II	Reading CO30/26R	Gosport & Fareham Omnibus Co	57	RP
GUF 191	1945	Guy Arab II	Northern Counties O30/26R	Southdown Motor Services	451	A
XUF 141	1960	Leyland Tiger Cub PSUC1/2	Weymann C41F	Southdown Motor Services	1141	R
70 AUF	1962	Commer Avenger IV	Harrington C—F	Southdown Motor Services	70	A
WTS 429A	1962	Commer Avenger IV	Harrington C35C	Southdown Motor Services	60	
WRJ 179	1963	Leyland Titan PD2/40	MCW H36/28F	Salford City Transport	179	RP
972 CUF	1964	Leyland Titan PD3/4	Northern Counties FH39/30F	Southdown Motor Services	972	RP
AOR 158B	1964	Leyland Titan PD3/4	Northern Counties FHO39/30F	Southdown Motor Services	412	RP
DRR 153B	1964	Leyland Titan PD3/4	Northern Counties FHO39/30F	Southdown Motor Services	419	R
PRX 190B	1964	Leyland Titan PD3/4	Northern Counties FHO39/30F	Southdown Motor Services	416	R
PRX 200B	1964	Leyland Titan PD3/4	Northern Counties FHO39/30F	Southdown Motor Services	418	R
PRX 206B	1964	Leyland Titan PD3/4	Northern Counties FHO39/30F	Southdown Motor Services	401	R
ZV 1461	1964	Leyland Titan PD3/4	Northern Counties FHO39/30F	Southdown Motor Services	415	RP
BUF 122C	1965	Leyland Leopard PSU3/1RT	Marshall B45F	Southdown Motor Services	122	RP
BUF 260C	1965	Leyland Titan PD3/4	Northern Counties FH39/30F	Southdown Motor Services	260	R
BUF 277C	1965	Leyland Titan PD3/4	Northern Counties FH39/30F	Southdown Motor Services	277	R
BUF 426C	1965	Leyland Titan PD3/4	Northern Counties FCO39/30F	Southdown Motor Services	426	R
CJN 436C	1965	Leyland Titan PD3/6	Massey H38/32R	Southend Corporation	336	
FCD 294D	1966	Leyland Titan PD3/4	Northern Counties FH39/29F	Southdown Motor Services	294	R
FCD 307D	1966	Leyland Titan PD3/4	Northern Counties FH-/-F	Southdown Motor Services	307	RP
KUF 199F	1968	Leyland Leopard PSU3/1RT	Willowbrook B45F	Southdown Motor Services	199	R
LFS 296F	1968	Bristol VRTLL6G	ECW O41/36F	Scottish Omnibuses (Eastern Scottish)	AA296	R
SYX 569F	1968	Leyland Leopard PSU4/4R	Duple C41F	Grey Green Coaches of London		A
PUF 165H	1969	Leyland Leopard PSU3/1RT	Northern Counties DP49F	Southdown Motor Services	465	RP
TCD 374J	1970	Daimler Fleetline CRG6LX	Northern Counties	Southdown Motor Services	374	RP
TCD 383J	1970	Daimler Fleetline CRG6LX	Northern Counties	Southdown Motor Services	383	RP
TCD 490J	1970	Bristol RESL6L	Marshall B45F	Southdown Motor Services	490	RP
BHH 83J	1971	Leyland Leopard PSU3B/4RT	Plaxton C47F	Southdown Motor Services	1835	RP
UUF 116J	1971	Bristol VRTSL6LX	ECW H-/-F	Southdown Motor Services	516	RP
SCD 731N	1974	Leyland Atlantean AN68/1R	Park Royal - Roe H43/30F	Southdown Motor Services	731	R
RUF 37R	1977	Leyland National 11351A/2R	Leyland National B44D	Southdown Motor Services	37	RP
OPV 821	1979	Leyland Leopard PSU3R/4RT	Plaxton C48F	Southdown Motor Services	1321	RP
USV 324	1979	Leyland Leopard PSU3R/4RT	Plaxton C48F	Southdown Motor Services	1320	RP

Notes:

EHO 869	Rebodied in 1953
WTS 429A	Originally registered 60 AUF
ZV 1461	Originally registered 415 DCD
PRX 200B	Originally registered 418 DCD
AOR 158B	Originally registered 412 DCD
PRX 190B	Originally registered 416 DCD
PRX 206B	Originally registered 401 DCD
DRR 153B	Originally registered 419 DCD
LFS 296F	Originally H47/32F.
UUF 116J	Originally H39/31F
BHH 83J	Originally registered UUF 335J
OPV 821	Originally registered EAP 921V
USV 324	Originally registered BYJ 920T

Telford Bus Group

Contact address: 47 Ian Road, Newchapel, Stoke-on-Trent, Staffs ST7 4PP

Brief description: The Telford Bus Group has a collection of privately-owned buses and coaches in various parts of England. The Group has become known for its Bedford VALs of which 12 examples are preserved, with examples of several body types. Other vehicles include Daimler Fleetline 'Mancunian', Seddon Pennine VI, Commer Avenger and Leyland Leopard 'Midland Red S27 type'. Not all vehicles are restored and some are long term projects.

Registration	Date	Chassis	Body	New to	Fleet No	Status
386 DD	1961	Bedford J2	Plaxton C20F	Talbott of Moreton-in-Marsh		RP
3190 UN	1962	Commer Avenger IV	Plaxton C41F	Wright of Penycae		RP
9797 DP	1964	Bedford VAL 14	Duple C52F	Smiths of Reading		RP
EHL 472D	1966	Bedford VAL 14	Plaxton C52F	West Riding Automobile Co	3	R
JTH 100F	1968	Bedford VAM 14	Duple C45F	Davies of Pencader		RP
UWX 981F	1968	Bedford VAL 70	Plaxton C52F	Mosley of Barugh Green		RP
RBC 345G	1969	Bedford VAL 70	Duple C52F	Cook of Dunstable		RP
WWY 115G	1969	Bedford VAL 70	Plaxton C53F	Abbey Coachways of Selby		R
FYG 663J	1970	Bedford VAL 70	Willowbrook B56F	Wigmore of Dinnington		RP
VBD 310H	1970	Bedford VAL 70	Plaxton C48F	Coales of Woolaston		RP
YYB 239H	1970	Bedford VAL 70	Caetano C53F	Clevedon Motorways of Clevedon		A
BHO 670J	1971	Bedford VAL 70	Duple C53F	Castle Coaches of Waterlooville		R
RAR 690J	1971	Bedford VAL 70	Van Hool C51F	All Seasons of London		R
RNA 236J	1971	Daimler Fleetline CRG6LXB-33	Park Royal H47/29D	SELNEC PTE	2236	A
CDC 166K	1972	Seddon Pennine VI	Plaxton C45F	Bob's of Middlesborough	26	RP
CDC 168K	1972	Seddon Pennine VI	Plaxton C41F	Bob's of Middlesborough	28	RP
FAR 724K	1972	Bedford VAL 70	Duple C53F	Langley Coaches of Slough		A
ANO 395L	1973	Bedford VAL 70	Plaxton C53F	Golden Boy Coaches of Roydon		A
JHA 227L	1973	Leyland Leopard PSU3B/2R	Marshall DP49F	Midland Red Omnibus Co	227	RP

Notes:

RNA 236J	Mancunian
ANO 395L	Caravan conversion

Bedford VALs were popular with independents large and small. This Plaxton Panorama-bodied VAL14 was No 3 in the West Riding fleet. *Philip Lamb*

Three Counties Bus and Commercial Vehicle Museum

Contact address: 83 Millwright Way, Flitwick, Beds MK45 1BQ
Phone: 01525 370578 or 01525 712091
E-mail: tcbm@lodekka.demon.co.uk
Affiliation: NARTM
Brief description: Established to provide a focus for bus preserva-

tion in Bedfordshire, Buckinghamshire and Hertfordshire. Seeks to ensure a long-term future for the vehicles and secure permanent undercover accommodation.
Events planned: Please see enthusiast press for planned Operating Days.

Registration	Date	Chassis	Body	New to	Fleet No	Status
FXT 122	1939	Leyland Cub REC	LPTB B20F	London Transport	CR16	RP
DBL 154	1946	Bristol K6A	ECW L27/28R	Thames Valley Traction Co	446	R
CFN 104	1947	Leyland Tiger PS1/1	Park Royal C32R	East Kent Road Car Co		R
LYR 915	1952	AEC Regent III O961 RT	Weymann H30/26R	London Transport	RT 3496	R
MXX 332	1952	Guy Special NLLVP	ECW B26F	London Transport	GS 32	R
MXX 434	1952	AEC Regal IV 9821LT RF	Metro Cammell B39F	London Transport	RF 457	R
MXX 489	1953	AEC Regal IV 9821LT RF	Metro Cammell B39F	London Transport	RF 512	RP
TUO 482	1956	Bristol LS5G	ECW B41F	Southern National Omnibus Co	1776	RP
OVL 473	1960	Bristol Lodekka FS5G	ECW H33/27RD	Lincolnshire Road Car Co	2378	R
DEK 3D	1966	Leyland Titan PD2/37	Massey H37/27F	Wigan Corporation	140	R
KBD 712D	1966	Bristol Lodekka FS6G	ECW H33/27RD	United Counties Omnibus Co	712	R
UXD 129G	1968	Bristol RELL6L	ECW B48D	Luton Corporation	129	RP
VLW 444G	1969	AEC Merlin 4P2R	MCW B25D	London Transport	MBS 444	A
FRM 499K	1972	Leyland National Demonstrator	Leyland National B45F	Leyland Research Fleet		A
NPD 127L	1973	Leyland National 1151/1R/0402	Leyland National B49F	London Country Bus Services	LNC27	A
SOA 674S	1977	Leyland Leopard PSU3E/4R	Plaxton C49F	Midland Red Omnibus Co	674	R

Notes:
TUO 482	Originally B45F. Reseated to B41F in 1964
FRM 499K	Converted to classroom by Leyland 1975

Representing the National Bus Company era is former Midland Red 674, A Plaxton Supreme-bodied Leyland Leopard. Philip Lamb

Wealdstone & District Vintage Vehicle Collection

Contact address: 91 Graham Road, Wealdstone, Middx HA3 5RE
E-mail: oldbusgarage@sftt.co.uk
Web site: www.sftt.co.uk/busgarage
Brief description: A small collection of mainly London buses from

the 1950s, examples of which regularly attend rallies. Anyone wishing to visit or assist with the vehicles is welcome. Please write to the address given.

Registration	Date	Chassis	Body	New to	Fleet No	Status
DL 9706	1935	Dennis Lancet	ECW B36R	Southern Vectis Omnibus Co	516	RP
KLB 716	1950	AEC Regent III O961 RT	Park Royal H30/26R	London Transport	RT 1594	R
KYY 622	1950	AEC Regent III O961 RT	Park Royal H30/26R	London Transport	RT 1784	R
MLL 817	1952	AEC Regal IV 9821LT RF	Metro Cammell B37F	London Transport	RF 280	R
MXX 410	1953	AEC Regal IV 9821LT RF	Metro Cammell B41F	London Transport	RF 433	R
MXX 430	1953	AEC Regal IV 9821LT RF	Metro Cammell B39F	London Transport	RF 453	R
NLE 939	1953	AEC Regent III O961 RT	Park Royal H30/26R	London Transport	RT 4275	RP

Notes:
DL 9706   Rebodied 1944

The West Country Historic Omnibus & Transport Trust

Contact address: The Secretary, 13 Dokkum Road, Crediton, Devon EX17 3DJ
Web site: www.busmuseum.org.uk
Affiliation: NARTM

Brief description: It is hoped to stage an event in September at a West Country location. Taking the form of a commercial vehicle rally, it will include heritage bus rides using vehicles of local origin/interest (please see web site).

Registration	Date	Chassis	Body	New to	Fleet No	Status
JUO 983	1948	Bristol LL6B	ECW FB39F	Southern National Omnibus Co	1218	RP
MOD 973	1952	Bristol LS6G	ECW C39F	Southern National Omnibus Co (Royal Blue)	1286	RP
TUO 217J	1970	Leyland Panther PSUR1B/1R	Marshall B—D	Devon General	217	R
A927 MDV	1983	Ford Transit 160D	Carlyle B16F	Devon General	7	R
C801 FRL	1985	Mercedes L608D	Reeve Burgess B20F	Western National Ltd	104	RP

Notes:
JUO 983   Rebodied 1958
TUO 217J   Ordered by Exeter City Transport. Converted to publicity vehicle in 1980.

West Midlands Bus Preservation Society

Contact address: Secretary, 5 Pommel Close, Walsall WS5 4QE
Brief description: The main core of the collection is of vehicles from the West Midlands PTE in the period 1969 to 1986. Other artefacts are being collected for inclusion in a planned transport museum.
Opening days/times: Vehicles can be viewed by special arrangement.

Registration	Date	Chassis	Body	New to	Fleet No	Status
VG 5541	1933	Bristol GJW	Weymann O28/26R	Norwich Electric Tramways		A
GKE 68	1939	Bristol K5G	Weymann H28/26R	Chatham & District Traction Co	874	A
DUK 278	1946	Guy Arab II	Roe H31/25R	Wolverhampton Corporation	378	RP
KHA 301	1948	BMMO C1	Duple C30C	BMMO ('Midland Red')	3301	R
GOU 732	1949	Tilling Stevens K6LA7	Scottish Aviation C33F	Altonian Coaches of Alton		R
LTA 813	1950	Bristol KS5G	ECW L27/28R	Western National Omnibus Co	994	R
OTT 43	1953	Bristol LS6G	ECW C39F	Western National Omnibus Co (Royal Blue)	2200	R
UHY 362	1955	Bristol KSW6B	ECW H32/28R	Bristol Tramways	8322	R
56 GUO	1961	Bristol MW6G	ECW C39F	Western National Omnibus Co (Royal Blue)	2267	RP
EHA 424D	1966	BMMO D9	BMMO/Willowbrook H40/32RD	BMMO ('Midland Red')	5424	R
NOV 880G	1969	Daimler Fleetline CRG6LX	Park Royal H43/29D	Birmingham City Transport	3880	RP
OTA 640G	1969	Bristol RELH6G	ECW C45F	Southern National Omnibus Co (Royal Blue)	2380	R
SOE 913H	1969	Daimler Fleetline CRG6LX-33	Park Royal H47/33D	West Midlands PTE	3913	A
TOB 986H	1970	Daimler Fleetline CRG6LX-33	Park Royal H—/—D	West Midlands PTE	3986	A
TOB 997H	1970	Daimler Fleetline CRG6LX-33	Park Royal H47/33D	West Midlands PTE	3997	RP
YOX 133K	1971	Daimler Fleetline CRG6LX	Park Royal H43/33F	West Midlands PTE	4133	A
NOB 413M	1974	Bristol VRTSL6LX	MCW H43/33F	West Midlands PTE	4413	A
NOC 600R	1976	Leyland Fleetline FE30AGR	Park Royal H43/33F	West Midlands PTE	6600	A
WDA 835T	1978	MCW Metrobus DR102/1	MCW H43/30F	West Midlands PTE	6835	RP
BOK 5V	1979	MCW Metrobus DR102/12	MCW H43/30F	West Midlands PTE	2005	
WDA 956T	1979	Leyland Fleetline FE30AGR	MCW B37F	West Midlands PTE	1956	A
WDA 986T	1979	Leyland Fleetline FE30AGR	MCW H43/33F	West Midlands PTE	6986	R

Notes:

VG 5541	Converted to Diesel 1938 and open top 1950
DUK 278	Rebodied 1952
TOB 997H	Gardner 6LXB engine fitted after acquisition by C J Partridge & Son of Hadleigh
TOB 986H	Converted to exhibition vehicle
WDA 835T	Exhibited at 1978 Commercial Motor Show
WDA 956T	Originally double deck bus (H43/33F) 6956; rebuilt as single-decker in 1994

Left: **The D9 was Midland Red's last double-decker to be produced in house in some numbers. Several, including 5424 are preserved.** *Philip Lamb*

West of England Transport Collection

Contact address: 15 Land Park, Chulmleigh, Devon, EX18 7BH
Affiliation: NARTM
Brief description: A large private collection of vehicles, mainly from West Country major operators. The collection includes buses, coaches and transport memorabilia.

Events planned: 6 October 2002 — Annual WETC Open Day
Opening days/times: Viewing at other times by prior arrangement with C. T. Shears, tel: 01769 580811.

Registration	Date	Chassis	Body	New to	Fleet No	Status
UO 2331	1927	Austin 20 5PL	Tiverton B13F	Sidmouth Motor Co		RP
VW 203	1927	Leyland Lion PLSC3	Mumford B—R	National Omnibus & Transport Co	2407	A
JY 124	1932	Tilling Stevens B10A2 Express	Beadle B—R	Western National Omnibus Co		A
OD 5489	1933	Vauxhall Cadet VY	Mount Pleasant	Davis of Rockbeare		R
OD 5868	1933	Leyland Lion LT5	Weymann B31F	Devon General	68	A
OD 7500	1934	AEC Regent O661	Brush H30/26R	Devon General	DR213	R
ADV 128	1935	Bristol JO5G	Beadle B—R	Western National Omnibus Co		A
ATT 922	1935	Bristol JJW6A	Beadle B35R	Western National Omnibus Co		RP
AUO 74	1935	Leyland Lion LT5A	(chassis only) -	Devon General	SL79	A
BOW 169	1938	Bristol L5G	-	Hants & Dorset Motor Services	TS676	A
EFJ 241	1938	Leyland Titan TD5	Leyland H30/26R	Exeter Corporation	26	A
EFJ 666	1938	Leyland Tiger TS8	Cravens B32R	Exeter Corporation	66	R
ETT 995	1938	AEC Regent O661 rebuild	Saunders Roe H30/26R	Devon General	DR705	A
EUF 204	1938	Leyland Titan TD5	Park Royal H28/26R	Southdown Motor Services	204	A
DOD 474	1940	AEC Regal 0662	Weymann B35F	Devon General	SR474	A
FTA 634	1941	Bristol K5G	ECW L27/28R	Western National Omnibus Co	345	RP
GTA 395	1941	Bristol LL5G	Brislington Body Works B39R	Southern National Omnibus Co	373	RP
JTA 314	1943	Guy Arab II	Roe H31/25RD	Devon General	DG314	A
DJY 965	1948	Crossley DD42/5	Crossley L27/26R	Plymouth Corporation	335	RP
GLJ 957	1948	Leyland Titan PD1A	ECW L27/26R	Hants & Dorset Motor Services	PD959	A
JFJ 606	1949	Daimler CVD6	Brush H30/26R	Exeter Corporation	43	A
MAF 544	1949	Austin CXB	Mann Egerton FC31C	J J Pollard of Hayle		RP
LUO 595	1950	AEC Regal III 6821A	Weymann B35F	Devon General	SR 595	RP
HJY 296	1953	Leyland Titan PD2/12	Leyland H30/26R	Plymouth Corporation	396	A
VDV 817	1957	AEC Regent V MD3RV	Metro Cammell H33/26R	Devon General	DR817	R
974 AFJ	1960	Guy Arab IV	Massey H31/26R	Exeter Corporation	74	R
1 RDV	1964	AEC Reliance 2MU3RA	Harrington C41F	Devon General Grey Cars	1	R
CTT 513C	1965	AEC Regent V 2D3RA	Park Royal H40/29F	Devon General	513	R
GNM 235N	1975	Bristol LHL6L	Plaxton C51F	Caroline Seagull of Great Yarmouth		R
MUN 742R	1976	AEC Reliance 6U3ZR	Plaxton C—F			R
CRM 927T	1979	Leyland/DAB	Leyland B64T	South Yorkshire PTE	2006	A
C748 FFJ	1985	Ford Transit 190D	Carlyle B16F	Devon General	748	A

Notes:

UO 2331	Body new 1933
VW 203	Body new 1936
JY 124	New body and engine fitted in 1947
OD 7500	Rebodied 1949
ATT 922	Rebodied in the late 1940s
ADV 128	Rebodied 1950
AUO 74	Front end of chassis only
ETT 995	Rebuilt in 1953 using prewar mechanical components and rebodied
BOW 169	New with Beadle body; acquired by Wilts & Dorset Motor Services (505) in 1952 and converted to breakdown vehicle in 1956
EFJ 666	Used as a snow plough 1952-6
EFJ 241	Converted to tree-cutter in 1958
EUF 204	Rebodied 1949
FTA 634	Damaged in 1941 by enemy action and rebuilt
GTA 395	Lengthened and rebodied in 1954
CTT 513C	Restored by the Oxford Bus Museum Trust
CRM 927T	Articulated prototype (57 ft long)

Right: **Winkleigh residents include from left to right: Devon General DR705, A Saunders–bodied AEC Regal 1 rebuild, a former Western National Beadle-bodied Tilling-Stevens B10 and Exeter 26, an all-Leyland TD5.** *Philip Lamb*

Right:
Newer buses at Winkleigh include Devon General 748, a Carlyle-bodied Ford Transit. *Philip Lamb*

Westgate Museum

Contact address: Enquiries: 14 Ilkley Road, Caversham, Reading RG4 7BD

Brief description: The collection, near Doncaster, is housed in a former Methodist Chapel built in 1865. The vehicles operate at Sandtoft Transport Centre from time to time.

Opening days/times: Viewing strictly by appointment.

Registration	Date	Chassis	Body	New to	Fleet No	Status
RC 8472+	1944	Sunbeam W	Weymann UH30/26R	Derby Corporation	172	R
SVS 281	1945	Daimler CWA6	Duple UH30/26R	Douglas Corporation	52	R
DRD 130+	1949	BUT 9611T	Park Royal H33/26RD	Reading Corporation	144	R
LDP 945	1955	AEC Regent III 6812A	Park Royal L31/26RD	Reading Corporation	98	R
WLT 529	1960	AEC Routemaster R2RH	Park Royal H36/28R	London Transport	RM529	R
+ Trolleybus						

Notes:
SVS 281   Originally registered FMN 955.

Part 3
Heritage
Buses
Services

Cumbria Classic Coaches stalwart, Alexander PA184 poses at Kirkby Stephen Midland station. The Leyland Tiger has an Alexander body.
Chris Dyson

Blue Triangle — Rainham

Contact address: Unit 3C, Denver Industrial Estate, Ferry Lane, Rainham, Essex, RM13 7MD.
Phone: 01708 631001

Operations planned for 2002: Sheduled heritage services not finalised at time of publication, but vehicles frequently appear on rail replacement services.

Registration	Date	Chassis	Body	New to	Fleet No	Status
HLW 178	1947	AEC Regent III O961 RT	Weymann H30/26R	London Transport	RT 191	R
KGK 959	1949	AEC Regent III O961 RT	Weymann H30/26R	London Transport	RT 2150	
KXW 171	1950	AEC Regent III O961 RT	Saunders Roe H30/26R	London Transport	RT 3062	
LLU 670	1950	AEC Regent III O961 RT	Park Royal H30/26R	London Transport	RT 3871	R
LYR 969	1952	AEC Regent III O961 RT	Weymann H30/26R	London Transport	RT 2799	
MXX 289	1952	AEC Regal IV 9821LT	Metro Cammell B39F	London Transport	RF 401	
WLT 900	1961	AEC Routemaster R2RH/1	Park Royal H36/28R	London Transport	RML 900	
CUV 260C	1965	AEC Routemaster R2RH/1	Park Royal H36/29RD	London Transport	RCL 2260	

Carmel Coaches — Okehampton

Contact address: Mr A. G. Hazell, Northlew, Okehampton, Devon.
Phone: 01409 221237

Operations planned for 2002: Route 174: Okehampton–Moretonhampstead.
Sundays and Bank Holidays, 26 May to 22 September.

Registration	Date	Chassis	Body	New to	Fleet No	Status
JFJ 875	1950	Daimler CVD6	Weymann B35F	Exeter City Transport	75	R
LOD 495	1950	Albion Victor FT39N	Duple C31F	Way of Crediton		R
MTT 640	1951	Leyland Titan PD2/1	Leyland L27/26R	Devon General	DL640	R

Carmel Coaches has operated this Duple–bodied Albion FT39N on its services for some years.
Carmel Coaches

Cosy Coaches — Killamarsh

Contact address: Cosy Coach Tours, 5 Meynell Way, Killamarsh, Derbyshire, S21 1HG.
Phone: 0114 248 9139
Operations planned for 2002: Sundays and Bank Holidays, 2 June to 26 August.
Bolsover Heritage Service: from Chesterfield station to Hardwick Hall, then circular via Bolsover Castle, returning to Hardwick Hall.
Fares: £5 for one complete circuit (with hop-on, hop-off facility).

Conections at Chesterfield station with trains from Sheffield and Nottingham.
Comprehensive timetables are available from the above address for £1 plus SAE.
Pre-booked tickets are available from Tourist Information Office, Low Pavement, Chesterfield, Derbyshire.

Registration	Date	Chassis	Body	New to	Fleet No	Status
ATS 408	1948	Bedford OB	Duple C29F	James Meffan of Kirriemuir		
DBW 613	1948	Bedford OB	Duple C29F	Oliver of Long Handborough		
MRB 765	1949	Bedford OB	Duple C29F	H D Andrew of Tideswell		
ERG 164	1950	Bedford OB	Duple C29F	Paterson of Aberdeen		
YBD 201	1961	Bristol MW6G	ECW C34F	United Counties Omnibus Co	201	

Cumbria Classic Coaches — Kirkby Stephen

Contact address: Bowber Head, Ravenstonedale, Kirkby Stephen, Cumbria, CA17 4NL.
Phone: 015396 23254
Website: www.cumbriaclassiccoaches.co.uk
E-mail: coaches@cumbriaclassiccoaches.co.uk

Operations planned for 2002: Route 569: Ravenstonedale–Kirkby Stephen–Hawes, Tues (Hawes market day) 17 April to 23 October.
Kendal Klipper (circular tour of Kendal), half-hourly, seven days a week 21 July to 13 September.
Eden Explorer, Weds 22 May to 25 September.

Registration	Date	Chassis	Body	New to	Fleet No	Status
WG 2373	1934	Leyland Lion LT5B	Burlingham B35F	W Alexander & Sons (Midland)	P169	R
CRN 80	1949	Leyland Tiger PS1	East Lancs B34R	Preston Corporation	75	R
TSK 763	1949	Commer Commando	Scottish Aviation C29F	David Lawson	C8	RP
CWG 286	1950	Leyland Tiger PS1/1	Alexander C35F	W Alexander & Sons (Northern)	PA184	R
627 HFM	1959	Bristol LD6B (6LXB)	ECW CO33/27R	Crosville	DLB 978	R

Notes:
WG 2373   Rebodied 1947
TSK 763   Original registration CMS 9. To be returned to original colours.
The company also uses Bristol L5G, KFM 767, on loan from Rexquote.

Green Bus Service — Great Wyrley

Contact address: Warstone Motors Ltd, The Garage, Jacobs Hall Lane, Great Wyrley, Staffordshire WS6 6AD
Phone: 01922 414141

Operations planned for 2002: School Summer Holidays:
Route 5 (Cannock–Telford) Thurs
Route 14 (Cannock–Lichfield) Fri

Registration	Date	Chassis	Body	New to	Fleet No	Status
GZ 2248	1944	Bedford OWB	Duple B32F	Northern Ireland Road Transport Board		
GCA 747	1950	Bedford OB	Duple C29F	Owen of Rhostyllen		
GNY 432C	1965	Leyland Titan PD3/4	Massey L35/35RD	Caerphilly Corporation	32	

Mac Tours — Edinburgh

Contact address: Edinburgh Vintage Bus Company, 11A James Court, Lawnmarket, Edinburgh EH1 2PB.
Phone: 0131 477 4771
Fax: 0131 220 0770

Operations planned for 2002: Hop-on, hop-off open-top tours of Edinburgh operate seven days a week, all year round.

Registration	Date	Chassis	Body	New to	Fleet No	Status
YSL 334	1951	Leyland Tiger PS1	Guernseybus OB35F	Jersey Motor Transport Co	44	RP
28231	1951	Leyland Tiger PS1	Guernseybus B35F	Jersey Motor Transport Co	49	RP

Registration	Date	Chassis	Body	New to	Fleet No	Status
833 AFM	1956	Bristol Lodekka LD6G	ECW O33/27RD	Crosville Motor Services	MG876	
LST 873	1958	Leyland Titan PD2/40	Park Royal O27/26RO	Barrow in Furness Corporation	166	
HSK 953	1959	Leyland Titan PD2/24	Glasgow Corporation O32/28R	Glasgow Corporation	L108	
JSJ 748	1959	AEC Routemaster R2RH	Park Royal O44/32R	London Transport	RM80	
JSJ 747	1959	AEC Routemaster R2RH	Park Royal O44/32R	London Transport	RM84	
JSJ 746	1959	AEC Routemaster R2RH	Park Royal O44/32R	London Transport	RM90	
VLT 163	1959	AEC Routemaster R2RH	Park Royal O44/32R	London Transport	RM163	
VLT 235	1959	AEC Routemaster R2RH	Park Royal O44/32R	London Transport	RM235	
WLT 371	1959	AEC Routemaster R2RH	Park Royal H36/28R	London Transport	RM371	RP
858 DYE	1960	AEC Routemaster R2RH	Park Royal O36/28R	London Transport	RM727	
EDS 221A	1961	AEC Routemaster R2RH	Park Royal O36/28R	London Transport	RM1010	
869 NHT	1961	Bristol Lodekka FS6G	ECW CO33/27RD	Bristol Omnibus Co	8579	
XSL 228A	1961	Bristol Lodekka FS6G	ECW CO33/27RD	Bristol Omnibus Co	8576	
FTE 631B	1964	Leyland Titan PD3/4	East Lancs H41/32F	Rawtenstall Corporation	31	
CUV 203C	1965	AEC Routemaster R2RH	Park Royal H36/28R	London Transport	RM2203	R
CUV 210C	1965	AEC Routemaster R2RH	Park Royal O36/28R	London Transport	RM2210	
CUV 248C	1965	AEC Routemaster R2RH/1	Park Royal CO36/29RD	London Transport	RCL2248	
DHC 784E	1967	Leyland Titan PD2A/30	East Lancs O32/28R	Eastbourne Corporation	84	
HFR 507E	1967	Leyland Titan PD3/A	Metro Cammell H41/30R	Blackpool Corporation	507	
NMY 646E	1967	AEC Routemaster R2RH/2	Park Royal H-/-F	British European Airways/LT	BEA46	
JTF 218F	1968	Leyland Titan PD2A/30	East Lancs O36/28R	Darwen Corporation		R
WRH 294J	1970	Leyland Atlantean PDR1A/1	Roe O43/28F	Kingston upon Hull Corporation	294	
ARH 304K	1970	Leyland Atlantean PDR1A/1	Roe O43/29F	Kingston upon Hull Corporation	304	
F572 RCW	1988	Optare City Pacer LT55	Optare B19F	Blackpool Transport	572	
F934 AWW	1989	Optare City Pacer LT55	Optare B25F	Blackpool Transport	583	

Notes:

YSL 334	Originally fitted with Reading B34F body and registered J 5567
28231	Originally fitted with Reading B34F body and registered J 5660
F934 AWW	Originally a demonstrator for Optare
LST 873	Originally registered CEO 952
HSK 953	Originally registered SGD 10
JSJ 748	Originally registered VLT 80
JSJ 747	Originally registered VLT 84
JSJ 746	Originally registered VLT 90
858 DYE	Originally registered WLT 727
EDS 221A	Originally registered 10 CLT
XSL 228A	Originally registered 866 NHT
NMY 646E	Originally seated H32/24F and was numbered RMA9 when with London Transport

Memory Lane Vintage Omnibus Services   Maidenhead

Contact address: 78 Lillibrooke Crescent, Maidenhead, Berkshire, SL6 3XQ.
Phone: 01628 825050
Fax: 01628 825851
E-mail: info@memorylane.co.uk

Operations planned for 2002: Route 32: Guildford–Dorking (with connections to Goodwyns and Strood Green, Sundays and Bank Holidays all year round.
Route 433: Guildford–Dorking, Summer Sundays and Bank Holidays (subject to confirmation from Surrey County Council)

Registration	Date	Chassis	Body	New to	Fleet No	Status
KGU 290	1949	AEC Regent III O961 RT	Weymann H30/26R	London Transport	RT 1530	
KYY 628	1950	AEC Regent III O961 RT	Park Royal H30/26R	London Transport	RT 1790	
LYF 377	1951	AEC Regal IV 9821LT	Metro Cammell B37F	London Transport	RF 26	
MLL 943	1952	AEC Regal IV 9821LT	Metro Cammell B39F	London Transport	RF 525	
MLL 952	1952	AEC Regal IV 9821LT RF	Metro Cammell B39F	London Transport	RF 315	
NLE 643	1953	AEC Regal IV 9821LT	Metro Cammell B39F	London Transport	RF 643	
617 DDV	1960	Bristol MW6G	ECW C39F	Southern National Omnibus Co (Royal Blue)	2250	

Registration	Date	Chassis	Body	New to	Fleet No	Status
VLT 216	1960	AEC Routemaster	Park Royal H—/—R	London Transport	RM216	
253 KTA	1962	Bristol MW6G	ECW C39F	Western National Omnibus Co (Royal Blue)	2270	
618 WTE	1962	AEC Reliance 2MU3RA	Plaxton DP41F	Lancashire United Transport	94	
AFN 764B	1964	AEC Regent V 2D3RA	Park Royal O40/32F	East Kent Road Car Co		
TYD 122G	1969	AEC Reliance 6MU3R	Willowbrook B45F	Hutchings & Cornelius Services of South Petherton		
TCD 376J	1970	Daimler Fleetline CRG6LX	Northern Counties O40/31F	Southdown Motor Services	376	
OJD 95R	1977	Bristol LH6L	ECW B33F	London Transport	BL95	

Note;

VLT 216   Converted to exhibition bus

Nostalgiabus   Mitcham

Contact address: Nostalgiabus Ltd, 4 Forual Close, Mitcham
CR4 4NE
Phone: 0208 640 6668

Fax: 0208 395 4415
Operations planned for 2002: To be confirmed

Registration	Date	Chassis	Body	New to	Fleet No	Status
KYE 905	1950	Bedford OB	Duple C27F	Grey Green		
MLL 523	1952	AEC Regal IV 9821LT RF	Metro Cammell B39F	London Transport	RF136	
MXX 367	1954	Guy Special NLLVP	ECW B26F	London Transport	GS67	
394 CLT	1963	AEC Routemaster R2RH	Park Royal H36/28R	London Transport	RM1394	
571 CLT	1963	AEC Routemaster R2RH	Park Royal H36/28R	London Transport	RM1571	
CUV 156C	1965	AEC Routemaster R2RH	Park Royal H36/28R	London Transport	RM2156	
CUV 180C	1965	AEC Routemaster R2RH	Park Royal H36/28R	London Transport	RM2180	

Note:

MLL 523   Prototype modernised RF, rebuilt 1965

Quantock Motor Services   Taunton

Contact address: Unit 82C, Taunton Trading Estate,
Norton Fitzwarren, Taunton TA2 6RX
Phone: 01823 251140
Fax: 01823 251833

Web site: www.heritagebus.co.uk
Operations planned for 2002: A subsidiary of rexquote, operations are principally private hire and contract. Local services are operated in Ilfracombe and Taunton — contact company for details.

Registration	Date	Chassis	Body	New to	Fleet No	Status
CYA 181J	1971	AEC Reliance 6MU4R	Plaxton B47F	Hutchings & Cornelius Services of South Petherton		
TDK 686J	1971	AEC Reliance 6U3ZR	Plaxton C57F	Yelloway Motor Services of Rochdale		
FDG 468L	1973	AEC Reliance 6MU4RA	Plaxton C45F	Cotterells of Mitcheldean		
MUR 217L	1973	AEC Reliance 6U3ZR	Plaxton C—F	Derek Randal of Acton		
UMP 903M	1973	AEC Reliance 6U3ZR	Willowbrook C53F	Lewis of Greenwich		
31908	1975	Bristol LH	Plaxton DP45F	Devon General	317	
31918	1975	Bristol LH	Plaxton DP45F	Devon General	321	
HVU 247N	1975	AEC Reliance 6U3ZR	Plaxton C53F	Yelloway Motor Services of Rochdale		
MPK 693P	1976	AEC Reliance 6U3ZR	Plaxton C53F	Edward Thomas of Ewell		
NNC 854P	1976	AEC Reliance 6U3ZR	Plaxton C49F	Yelloway Motor Services of Rochdale		
NNN 9P	1976	AEC Reliance 6U3ZR	Plaxton C53F	Derby City Transport (Blue Bus Services)		
TPT 6R	1976	AEC Reliance 6U3ZR	Plaxton C53F	Wilbys Coaches of Brigg		
APT 834S	1977	AEC Reliance 6U3ZR	Plaxton C53F	Gardiner of Spennymoor		
RCV 283R	1977	AEC Reliance 6U3ZR	Plaxton C55F	National Travel (East)		
TPD 28S	1977	AEC Reliance 6U2R	Duple C49F	London Country Bus Services		
VMJ 967S	1977	AEC Reliance 6U3ZR	Plaxton C53F	Lewis of Greenwich		
ANA 5T	1978	AEC Reliance 6U3ZR	Plaxton C53F	Charterplan		

Registration	Date	Chassis	Body	New to	Fleet No	Status
BUR 438T	1978	AEC Reliance	Plaxton C42F	Best of London		
TIJ 687	1978	AEC Reliance 6U3ZR	Plaxton C46F	Jalna of Church Gresley		
VPH 53S	1978	AEC Reliance 6U2R	Duple C49F	London Country Bus Services		
EBM 448T	1979	AEC Reliance 6U3ZR	Plaxton C57F			
GNK 781T	1979	AEC Reliance 6U3ZR	Duple C53F	Olde Luton		
JLT 150T	1979	Bristol LHS	Plaxton C35F	Harris of Grays		
WDK 562T	1979	AEC Reliance 6U3ZR	Plaxton C53F	Yelloway Motor Services of Rochdale		
YPL 105T	1979	AEC Reliance 6U2R	Duple DP49F	London Country Bus Services		
YPL 78T	1979	AEC Reliance 6U2R	Duple DP49F	London Country Bus Services		
YPL 92T	1979	AEC Reliance 6U2R	Duple DP49F	London Country Bus Services		
MDG 227V	1980	AEC Reliance 6U3ZR	Van Hool C57F	Central of Ledbury		
NUB 93V	1980	AEC Reliance 6U3ZR	Plaxton C53F	Compass of Wakefield		
ODV 404W	1981	AEC Reliance 6U2R	Duple DP53F	Tillingbourne		
A198 TAR	1984	AEC Reliance 6U3ZR	Berkhof (Ensign) C53F	East Kent Road Car Co		

Notes:

HVU 247N	Did carry registration 146FLD
31918	Guernsey Registration. Originally registered JFJ501N
31908	Guernsey Registration. Originally registered JFJ497N
NNN 9P	Originally C49F
RCV 283R	Originally registered OKY64R, later 176XYD.
BUR 438T	Known as 'Bert'
ANA 5T	Known as 'Anna'
NUB 93V	Known as 'Tabatha'
A198 TAR	Chassis new 1973 as HFN53L with Duple body. Rebodied 1984

Rexquote Heritage — Wiveliscombe

Contact address: Bishop's Lydeard, Somerset.
Phone: 01823 251140
Operations planned for 2002: Heritage vehicles will be used on services in the Taunton area during the summer

Event attending: 3/4 August 2002 — Steam & Vintage Rally, Bishops Lydeard

Registration	Date	Chassis	Body	New to	Fleet No	Status
BTF 24	1937	Leyland Lion LT7c	Leyland B34R	Lytham St Annes Corporation	4	A
JG 9938	1937	Leyland Tiger TS8	Park Royal C32R	East Kent Road Car Co		R
AJA 132	1938	Bristol L5G	Burlingham B35R	North Western Road Car Co	372	R
HKL 819	1946	AEC Regal I O662	Beadle O35F	Maidstone & District Motor Services		R
EMW 893	1947	Daimler CVD6	Park Royal B35C	Swindon Corporation	57	A
HUO 510	1947	AEC Regal I O662	Weymann B35F	Devon General	SR510	R
JUO 992	1947	Leyland Titan PD1	ECW L27/26R	Southern National Omnibus Co	2932	A
ACH 441	1948	AEC Regal III	Windover C32F	Trent Motor Traction Co	611	R
BWG 323	1948	Leyland Tiger PS1	Alexander C35F	W Alexander & Sons (Northern)		A
JFM 575	1948	AEC Regal III	Strachan B35R	Crosville Motor Services		RP
JTE 546	1948	AEC Regent III 6811A	Park Royal H33/26R	Morecambe & Heysham Corporation	20	R
JUP 233	1948	AEC Regal III 6821A	Burlingham B35F	Gillet & Baker of Quarrington Hill		R
CFN 121	1949	Dennis Lancet J3	Park Royal B35R	East Kent Road Car Co		R
JLJ 402	1949	Leyland Tiger PS2/3	Burlingham FDP35F	Bournemouth Corporation	45	R
KTF 594	1949	AEC Regent III 9621E	Park Royal O33/26R	Morecambe & Heysham Corporation	65	R
LJH 665	1949	Dennis Lancet J3	Duple C35F	Lee of Barnet		RP
CHL 772	1950	Daimler CVD6	Willowbrook DP35F	Bullock of Featherstone		R
GWN 432	1950	Dennis Lancet J3	Thurgood FC37F	Super of Tottenham		R
KFM 767	1950	Bristol L5G	ECW B35R	Crosville Motor Services	KG117	R
KFM 893	1950	Bristol L5G	ECW B35R	Crosville Motor Services	KG131	R
LFM 302	1950	Leyland Tiger PS1	Weymann B35F	Crosville Motor Services	KA226	R
LFM 717	1950	Bristol L5G	ECW B35R	Crosville Motor Services	KG136	A
LFM 724	1950	Bristol L5G	ECW B35R	Crosville Motor Services	KG143	A

Registration	Date	Chassis	Body	New to	Fleet No	Status
LFM 734	1950	Bristol LL5G	ECW B39R	Crosville Motor Services	KG153	A
DCK 219	1951	Leyland Titan PD2/3	East Lancs FCL27/22RD	Ribble Motor Services	1248	RP
FMO 949	1951	Bristol LL6B	ECW B39F	Thames Valley Traction Co	567	R
ADV 854A	1953	Leyland Titan PD2/12	Leyland H30/26R	Plymouth Corporation	397	A
CHG 545	1954	Leyland Tiger PS2/14	East Lancs B39F	Burnley Colne & Nelson	45	R
NLJ 271	1954	Leyland Royal Tiger PSU1/13	Burlingham B42F	Bournemouth Corporation	261	R
JVH 378	1955	AEC Regent III	East Lancs H33/28R	Huddersfield Joint Omnibus Committee	178	
838 AFM	1957	Bristol Lodekka LD6G	ECW H33/27RD	Crosville Motor Services	MG881	R
ACA 303A	1957	Bristol Lodekka LD6G	ECW H33/27RD	Crosville Motor Services	MG891	A
VDV 752	1957	Bristol Lodekka LDL6G	ECW O37/33RD	Western National Omnibus Co	1935	R
VDV 753	1957	Bristol Lodekka LDL6G	ECW O37/33RD	Western National Omnibus Co	1936	R
GSU 678	1958	Leyland Titan PD2/40	Metro Cammell	Portsmouth Corporation	114	A
NDB 356	1958	Leyland Tiger Cub PSUC1/1	Crossley B44F	Stockport Corporation	403	R
120 JRB	1959	Daimler Freeline D650HS	Burlingham C37F	Tailby & George ('Blue Bus Services') Willington		A
501 BTA	1959	Bristol Lodekka LD6G	ECW H33/27RD	Western National Omnibus Co	1949	A
503 BTA	1959	Bristol Lodekka LD6G	ECW H33/27RD	Western National Omnibus Co	1951	RP
890 ADV	1959	AEC Reliance 2MU3RV	Willowbrook C41F	Devon General Grey Cars	TCR890	RP
LDB 796	1960	Leyland Tiger Cub PSUC1	Willowbrook DP43F	North Western Road Car Co		R
536 JHU	1961	Bristol MW5G	ECW B45F	Bristol Omnibus Co	2514	R
RDB 846	1961	AEC Reliance 2MU3RA	Alexander DP41F	North Western Road Car Co	846	A
WKG 287	1961	AEC Reliance 2MU3RA	Willowbrook B41F	Western Welsh Omnibus Co	1287	A
3655 NE	1962	Leyland Tiger Cub PSUC1/12	Park Royal DP38D	Manchester City Transport	55	A
569 EFJ	1962	AEC Reliance 2MU4RA	Harrington C40F	Greenslades Tours of Exeter		A
572 CNW	1962	Daimler CVG6LX-30	Roe H39/31F	Leeds City Transport	572	A
AFE 719A	1962	AEC Reliance 2MU3RV	Weymann O40F	Maidstone & District Motor Services	S325	R
CYD 724C	1965	AEC Reliance 2MU4RA	Harrington C41F	Hutchings & Cornelius Services of South Petherton		R
HJA 965E	1967	Leyland Titan PD2/40	East Lancs Neepsend H36/28R	Stockport Corporation	65	R
KTA 986V	1980	Leyland Leopard PSU3E/4R	Plaxton DP49Ft	Devon General		A

Notes:

HKL 819	Originally B35F. Converted to open top in 1958 and renumbered OR1
KFM 893	Used as a tow bus
GWN 432	Rebodied 1960
FMO 949	Prototype conversion to front entrance by ECW
DCK 219	White Lady double deck coach
ADV 854A	Used by Southern National as a driver training bus
NLJ 271	Converted to OMO in 1960 when rear entrance was removed
GSU 678	Converted to breakdown vehicle. Originally registered ORV991
AFE 719A	Originally registered 325NKT. Converted to open top in 1974
572 CNW	Converted to exhibition vehicle
KTA 986V	Originally registered FDV803V

Southcoast Motor Services — Croydon

Contact address: PO Box 1029, Croydon, CR9 6AA
Phone: 0870 3215767
Operations planned for 2002: Route 77: Brighton (Palace Pier)–Devil's Dyke, Sundays and Bank Holidays 21 April to 29 September.
Other services as advertised in the enthusiast press.

Registration	Date	Chassis	Body	New to	Fleet No	Status
WRU 702B	1964	Leyland Titan PD3/4	Northern Counties FCO39/30F	Southdown Motor Services	406	
HCD 350E	1967	Leyland Titan PD3/4	Northern Counties FH39/30F	Southdown Motor Services	350	

Indices

Dover Transport Museum buses invade Canterbury bus station. *Philip Lamb*

Index of Vehicles by Registration Number

Reg	Page	Reg	Page	Reg	Page	Reg	Page
1 RDV	108	335 AOW	102	574 TD	54	833 AFM	114
105 UTU	65	340 TJO	80	595 LCG	86	8340 U	85
116 JTD	46	3655 NE	117	596 LCG	86	838 AFM	117
116 TMD	92	371 BKA	92	603 CYS	87	850 ABK	52
120 JRB	117	372 BKA	92	6162 RU	75	851 FNN	50
122 JTD	46	375 GWN	79	6167 RU	75	858 DYE	114
1252 EV	59	386 DD	104	617 DDV	114	861 HAL	50
1294 RE	16	3916 UB	91	618 WTE	115	862 RAE	22
1322 WA	64	394 CLT	115	6219 TF	54	866 HAL	50
14 LFC	52	3945 UE	26	6220 KW	39	869 NHT	114
14 PKR	88	404 RIU	67	6249 UP	95	871 KHA	21
1425 P	56	414 CLT	46	627 HFM	113	872 ATA	83
152 CLT	54	422 CAX	65	6314 HA	16	875 VFM	92
191 AWL	80	4227 FM	54	6330 WJ	64	881 BTF	96
194 BFC	80	433 MDT	57	6370 HA	18	8859 VR	54
201 YTE	54	434 BTE	54	6545 HA	21	8860 VR	46
2206 OI	32	436 KOV	18	657 BWB	57	890 ADV	117
221 JVK	95	453 AUP	54	66	57	891 VFM	92
248 NEA	21	462 EOT	72	675 COD	79	9 RDV	83
253 KTA	114	4632 VM	46	694 ZO	67	904 OFM	22
256 SFM	92	488 KOT	72	70 AUF	103	913 DTT	83
264 ERY	16	501 BTA	117	70 JZL	880	918 NRT	23
264 KTA	79	501 KD	92	71 AHI	26	924 AHY	85
28231	113	503 BTA	117	72 MMJ	91	931 GTA	83
297 LJ	75	503 RUO	83	7209 PW	65	932 GTA	83
3016 HA	21	504 EBL	48	737 DYE	43	935 GTA	83
3035 HA	16	507 OHU	22	7424 SP	60	943 KHA	21
304 GHN	74	5073 HA	21	756 KFC	52	952 JUB	42
304 KFC	52	5228 NW	85	760 CTD	90	956 AJO	52
305 KFC	52	528 CTF	96	773 FHA	16	960 HTT	83
312 MFC	80	536 JHU	117	78 D140	26	9629 WU	56
318 AOW	102	557 BNG	32	78 D824	26	964 H87	56
3190 UN	104	56 GUO	107	7874 WJ	64	966 RVO	16
31908	115	561 TD	90	80 NVO	50	972 CUF	103
31918	115	562 RTF	54	802 MHW	21	974 AFJ	108
324 NJO	80	569 EFJ	117	8154 EL	75	975 CWL	80
326 CAA	86	569 KKK	31	8156 EL	75	9797 DP	104
332 RJO	80	571 CLT	115	8159 EL	75	980 DAE	22
333 CRW	47	572 CNW	117	827 BWY	79	99-64-HB	21
334 CRW	16	574 CNW	85	828 SHW	88		

Reg	Page	Reg	Page	Reg	Page	Reg	Page
A198 TAR	116	ADV 128	108	AHA 582	19	ANA 5T	115
A706 LNC	46	ADV 854A	117	AHC 442	27	ANB 851	16
A765 NNA	101	ADX 1	36	AHE 163	42	ANO 395L	104
A869 SUL	52	ADX 196	36	AHF 850	68	ANQ 778	53
A927 MDV	106	ADX 63B	36	AHL 694	84	ANW 682	39
AAA 503C	72	AEK 514	39	AHN 451B	74	AOG 679	16
AAA 506C	72	AEL 170B	75	AHU 803	77	AOR 157B	82
AAA 508C	72	AFE 719A	117	AHW 200V	23	AOR 158B	103
AAA 756	58	AFJ 732T	79	AIT 934	67	APA 46B	50
ABD 253B	79	AFM 103G	54	AJA 132	116	APR 167A	50
ABR 433	94	AFM 106G	54	AJA 139B	54	APT 834S	115
ACA 303A	117	AFN 488B	31	AJA 152	44	APW 829B	36
ACB 902	53	AFN 764B	115	AJA 408L	99	ARD 676	78
ACB 904	96	AFN 777B	31	AJX 369	91	ARG 17B	60
ACC 88	53	AFN 780B	31	ALJ 340B	75	ARH 304K	114
ACH 441	116	AFS 91B	60	ALJ 973	78	ARN 392	53
ACK 796	96	AFT 930	95	ALJ 986	32	ARN 811C	96
AC-L 379	78	AFY 971	52	AML 582H	43	ASC 665B	60
ACU 304B	95	AH 79505	32	ANA 1Y	101	ATD 281J	91
AD 7156	52	AHA 451J	64	ANA 551Y	55	ATD 683	52

Reg	Page	Reg	Page	Reg	Page	Reg	Page
ATF 477	58	BPV 9	36	CFN 104	105	CWX 671	39
ATS 408	113	BR 7132	14	CFN 121	116	CXX 171	29
ATT 922	108	BRM 596	85	CFR 590C	54	CYA 181J	115
AUD 310J	80	BRS 37	58	CGJ 188	29	CYD 724C	117
AUF 666	36	BT 8939	93	CHF 565	68	CYI 621	67
AUO 74	108	BTF 24	116	CHG 541	59	CYJ 252	59
AUX 296	58	BTN 113	94	CHG 545	117	D122 PTT	52
AVH 470	85	BTR 361B	102	CHL 772	116	D63 NOF	46
AVX 975G	23	BUF 122C	103	CJG 959	31	DAU 370C	50
AWA 124B	60	BUF 260C	103	CJN 436C	103	DB 5070	44
AWG 393	58	BUF 277C	103	CK 3825	44	DBA 214C	46
AWG 623	58	BUF 426C	103	CK 4518	93	DBA 227C	88
AWG 639	58	BUR 438T	116	CKG 193	78	DBE 187	42
AXJ 857	44	BUS 181	87	CLE 122	43	DBL 154	105
AXM 649	43	BWG 323	116	CN 2870	19	DBN 978	65
AXM 693	29	BWG 39	58	CN 4740	94	DBU 246	53
AYV 651	43	BWG 833L	60	CN 6100	94	DBW 613	113
AZD 203	26	BWO 585B	65	CNG 125C	36	DCK 219	117
B106 XJO	52	BWS 105L	60	CNH 699	22	DCN 83	94
B401 NJF	14	BWU 691H	41	CNH 860	79	DCS 616	58
B926 KWM	68	BXA 452B	60	CNH 862	79	DDB 174C	46
BBA 560	44	BXA 464B	60	CPM 61	48	DDM 652	16
BBK 236B	27	BXD 576	43	CPO 100W	27	DED 797	53
BCB 341	53	C 2367	93	CPU 979G	23	DEK 3D	105
BCD 820L	48	C45 HDT	57	CRC 911	65	DEL 893C	79
BCK 367C	54	C519 FFJ	83	CRG 811	96	DFE 383	42
BCK 939	56	C526 DYT	43	CRM 927T	108	DFE 963D	22
BCP 671	91	C724 JJO	52	CRN 80	113	DFM 347H	54
BCR 379K	102	C729 JJO	80	CRR 819	50	DFV 146	90
BD 209	93	C748 FFJ	108	CRS 834	96	DGS 536	58
BDJ 67	53	C751 YBA	101	CRU 103C	75	DGS 625	58
BDJ 808	53	C801 FRL	106	CRU 180C	75	DHC 784E	114
BDJ 87	56	CAH 923	36	CRU 187C	76	DHD 177	39
BDY 809	32	CAP 234	37	CSG 29C	60	DHJ 301B	82
BED 731C	54	CBA 966L	85	CSG 773S	62	DHN 475	84
BEN 177	44	CBC 921	14	CSG 792S	62	DHR 192	48
BFE 419	42	CBD 778K	21	CTF 627B	91	DHW 293K	78
BFS 1L	60	CBR 539	94	CTP 200	27	DIU 83	67
BFS 463L	60	CBV 431	53	CTT 23C	83	DJF 349	50
BG 8557	68	CC 1087	93	CTT 513C	108	DJP 754	46
BG 9225	68	CC 7745	19	CTT 518C	50	DJY 965	108
BHA 399C	21	CC 8671	72	CU 3593	78	DKC 305L	54
BHA 656C	21	CC 9305	31	CUH 856	39	DKT 11	39
BHH 83J	103	CC 9424	72	CUL 260	32	DKY 703	56
BHL 682	84	CCD 940	82	CUS 297X	88	DKY 704	78
BHO 670J	104	CCG 296K	72	CUS 302X	88	DKY 706	56
BHU 92C	22	CCG 704C	86	CUV 156C	115	DKY 711	75
BJA 425	44	CCK 359	96	CUV 180C	115	DKY 712	75
BJK 674D	88	CCK 663	90	CUV 203C	114	DKY 713	53
BK 2986	27	CCX 777	85	CUV 208C	85	DL 5084	36
BKC 236K	92	CCX 801	85	CUV 210C	114	DL 9015	37
BMS 222	59	CD 4867	14	CUV 219C	21	DL 9706	106
BMS 405	58	CD 5125	14	CUV 229C	43	DLJ 111L	76
BNC 960T	101	CDB 224	44	CUV 233C	23	DLJ 116L	76
BND 874C	46	CDC 166K	104	CUV 248C	114	DLJ 119L	76
BNE 729N	99	CDC 168K	104	CUV 260C	112	DLU 92	29
BNE 751N	99	CDH 501	16	CVF 874	36	DM 2583	93
BNE 764N	99	CDJ 878	54	CVH 741	56	DM 6228	96
BOK 1V	21	CDK 409C	91	CVP 207	19	DMS 820	58
BOK 5V	107	CDL 479C	37	CWG 206	44	DMS 823	58
BON 474C	21	CDR 679	58	CWG 283	58	DNF 204	65
BOW 162	75	CDT 636	56	CWG 286	113	DNF 708C	99
BOW 169	108	CDX 516	29	CWG 720V	88	DOD 474	108
BOW 507C	102	CET 613	98	CWH 717	44	DPT 848	94
BP 9822	14	CFK 340	94	CWN 629C	22	DPV 68D	36
BPV 10	36	CFM 354	39	CWU 146T	68	DR 4902	48

DRC 224	32	EOD 524D	50	FFY 401	53	GE 2446	58
DRD 130	109	EOI 4857	68	FFY 402	19	GEA 174	22
DRN 289	96	ERD 152	56	FFY 403	53	GEN 201	54
DRR 153B	103	ERG 164	113	FFY 404	53	GFM 180C	92
DSD 936V	62	ERN 700	96	FGS 59D	59	GFN 273	31
DSG 169	58	ERV 247D	76	FHF 451	68	GFN 546N	31
DTP 823	27	ERV 249D	76	FHF 456	54	GFU 692	56
DU 4838	51	ERV 251D	76	FHN 833	42	GFY 406	53
DUK 278	107	ERV 252D	76	FHT 15D	22	GGA 670	58
DUK 833	22	ERV 938	32	FJJ 774	43	GGE 156T	88
DWB 54H	64	ESF 647W	62	FJW 616	19	GGG 300N	88
DWG 526	58	ESF 801C	60	FJY 915E	76	GGR 103N	95
DWH 706W	101	ESG 652	58	FKF 801D	92	GHA 327D	22
DX 3988	35	ETJ 108	58	FKF 835E	92	GHA 337	19
DX 5610	35	ETO 452C	50	FKF 933G	92	GHA 415D	21
DX 5629	35	ETT 995	108	FKU 758	56	GHD 765	64
DX 6591	35	EUD 256K	52	FMO 949	117	GHN 189	74
DX 7812	35	EUF 184	14	FON 630	16	GHN 574	56
DX 8871	48	EUF 198	39	FPT 6G	96	GHT 154	77
DY 5029	88	EUF 204	108	FR 1347	48	GJ 2098	29
E815 WDV	83	EUP 405B	95	FRB 211H	21	GJB 254	52
EA 4181	16	EVA 324	58	FRC 956	19	GJB 279	68
EBM 448T	116	EVD 406	39	FRJ 254D	46	GJG 751D	31
EBO 919	78	EVL 549E	42	FRJ 511	65	GJX 331	39
ECD 524	27	EWM 358	53	FRM 499K	105	GK 3192	43
ECU 201E	95	EWS 130D	60	FRU 305	66	GK 5323	43
ECX 425	89	EWS 168D	60	FSC 182	58	GK 5486	43
ED 6141	52	EX 6644	53	FSU 102T	88	GKD 434	92
EDB 549	44	EXV 201	32	FTA 634	108	GKE 68	107
EDB 562	44	EXV 253	43	FTB 11	52	GKP 511	56
EDB 575	44	EZH 155	26	FTE 631B	114	GLJ 957	108
EDS 221A	114	EZH 17	67	FTO 614	56	GM 5875	68
EDS 288A	60	EZH 170	26	FTR 511	102	GM 6384	59
EDS 320A	59	EZH 231	67	FTT 704	77	GNC 276N	46
EDS 50A	59	EZH 64	67	FVH 1	85	GNF 15V	101
EDT 703	56	EZL 1	67	FW 5698	42	GNF 16V	101
EDV 555D	79	F572 RCW	114	FW 8990	56	GNK 781T	116
EED 8	53	F685 YOG	18	FWG 846	59	GNM 235N	108
EF 7380	94	F934 AWW	114	FWL 371E	52	GNY 432C	113
EFJ 241	108	FAR 724K	104	FWW 596	39	GO 5198	43
EFJ 666	108	FBG 910	68	FWX 914	39	GOU 732	107
EFJ 92	44	FBN 232C	75	FXH 521	32	GOU 845	72
EFN 591	31	FBR 53D	95	FXT 122	105	GRS 343E	60
EFV 300	89	FBU 827	53	FYG 663J	104	GRY 60D	21
EGA 79	48	FC 2602	51	FYS 839	78	GSC 658X	62
EGN 369J	29	FCD 294D	103	FYS 988	48	GSC 667X	62
EGO 426	29	FCD 307D	103	FYS 996	87	GSI 353	67
EGP 1J	43	FCI 323	26	FYS 998	48	GSU 678	117
EHA 415D	18	FCK 844	96	FYS 999	87	GTA 395	108
EHA 424D	107	FCK 884	96	FZ 7897	68	GTP 175F	102
EHA 767D	21	FDG 468L	115	GAA 580	72	GTV 666	56
EHA 775	16	FDL 927D	37	GAA 616	72	GTX 761W	50
EHL 344	84	FDM 724	19	GAJ 12	56	GUE 247	19
EHL 472D	104	FDO 573	42	GAL 967	58	GUF 191	103
EHO 228	27	FDV 829V	83	GAM 216	22	GUJ 608	16
EHO 869	103	FEA156	22	GAV 254	34	GUP 907N	95
EHV 65	27	FEL 105L	76	GAX 2C	79	GUX 188	67
EKU 743	56	FEL 209V	76	GAY 171	14	GVD 47	58
EKU 746	56	FEL 751D	50	GBJ 192	32	GW 713	48
EKV 966	47	FES 831W	62	GBU 1V	101	GWJ 724	64
EKY 558	56	FET 617	98	GCA 747	113	GWN 432	116
ELP 228	29	FET 618	56	GCD 48	82	GYC 160K	23
EMW 893	116	FFM 135C	54	GCM 152E	68	GZ 2248	113
EN 9965	99	FFM 136C	54	GDJ 435	54	GZ 7638	66
END 832D	99	FFU 860	42	GDL 764	37	HA 3501	19
ENW 980D	39	FFV 447D	60	GDT 421	56	HA 4963	16

Code	No.	Code	No.	Code	No.	Code	No.
HA 8047	51	HUO 510	116	JO 5032	51	KBD 712D	105
HAH 537L	79	HUP 236	94	JO 5403	51	KBO 961	78
HAX 399N	23	HUS 675	87	JOJ 222	16	KCG 627L	72
HBD 919T	79	HUS 676	87	JOJ 245	19	KCK 869	96
HBF 679D	21	HVH 234	85	JOJ 257	16	KCK 914	96
HCD 347E	82	HVH 472D	89	JOJ 526	16	KD 3185	88
HCD 350E	117	HVM 901F	46	JOJ 533	19	KDB 408F	46
HCK 204G	54	HVU 244N	46	JOJ 548	16	KDJ 999	54
HD 7905	64	HVU 247N	115	JOJ 847	16	KDL 885F	37
HDG 448	19	HW 6634	22	JOJ 976	19	KDT 206D	57
HDJ 753	54	HWO 334	19	JOV 613P	21	KDT 393	56
HDK 835	44	HWV 294	79	JOV 714P	18	KED 546F	90
HDV 639E	60	HX 2756	43	JOW 499E	102	KEL 110	75
HE 12	93	HYM 768	43	JOW 928	102	KEL 127	75
HEK 705	46	HYM 812	78	JP 4712	44	KEL 131	16
HET 513	48	HZA 230	67	JPA 190K	29	KEL 133	75
HF 9126	58	HZA 279	67	JPT 544	94	KET 220	64
HFL 672L	18	HZD 593	67	JRJ 281E	46	KFF 367	68
HFO 742	21	IB 552	14	JRN 41	96	KFM 767	116
HFO659	58	IIL 4595	62	JRR 404	19	KFM 775	19
HFR 507E	114	ILI 98	26	JRR 930	50	KFM 893	116
HFR 512E	91	IY 1940	67	JRT 82K	36	KGK 529	98
HFR 515E	91	IY 7383	26	JSC 900E	60	KGK 575	98
HG 9651	65	IY 7384	67	JSF 928T	62	KGK 803	29
HGA 983D	88	IY 8044	26	JSJ 746	114	KGK 959	112
HGC 130	29	J 1359	59	JSJ 747	114	KGM 664F	60
HGD 894L	88	J 2503	49	JSJ 748	114	KGU 290	114
HGM 335E	60	JA 7585	44	JSX 595T	62	KGY 4D	43
HGM 346E	60	JAA 708	86	JT 8077	37	KHA 301	107
HHA 637	19	JBN 153	46	JTA 314	108	KHA 352	16
HHN 202	94	JC 5313	88	JTD 300B	54	KHC 369	57
HHP 755	91	JCK 530	96	JTE 546	116	KHL 855	85
HJA 965E	117	JCK 542	96	JTF 218F	114	KHU 326P	23
HJY 296	108	JCP 60F	48	JTF 920B	57	KHW 306E	21
HKF 820	92	JDJ 260K	54	JTH 100F	104	KHW 630	22
HKL 819	116	JDN 668	56	JUB 29	91	KID 154	26
HKR 11	56	JEL 257	22	JUE 349	19	KJ 2578	52
HKW 82	39	JF 2378	16	JUO 983	106	KJA 299G	54
HLJ 44	75	JFJ 506N	79	JUO 992	116	KJA 871F	46
HLW 159	53	JFJ 606	108	JUP 233	116	KJD 401P	43
HLW 178	112	JFJ 875	112	JV 9901	56	KLB 716	106
HLX 410	29	JFM 238D	34	JVF 528	51	KLB 908	98
HNB 24N	101	JFM 575	116	JVH 378	117	KLB 915	98
HNW 131D	39	JFM 650J	54	JVH 381	39	KLJ 346	75
HOD 30	39	JG 8720	72	JVO 230	50	KMN 519	92
HOR 493	86	JG 9938	116	JVS 541	60	KNG 374	36
HOR 590E	86	JHA 227L	104	JVU 775	44	KNV 337	79
HOR 592E	86	JHA 868E	21	JVW 976W	82	KOD 585	83
HOU 904	72	JHA 890	16	JWB 416	64	KOM 150	47
HOV 685	19	JHL 708	84	JWS 594	58	KON 311P	21
HPW 108	78	JHL 983	85	JWU 244N	89	KOU 791P	23
HPW 133	42	JKC 178	92	JWU 886	39	KOW 910F	102
HRG 209	59	JLJ 402	116	JWW 375	56	KOX 663F	18
HRN 249G	96	JLJ 403	75	JWW 376	56	KOX 780F	21
HRN 31	96	JLT 150T	116	JWW 377	56	KPM 91E	60
HRN 39	96	JMA 413L	54	JWX 599	58	KPT 909	48
HRS 265V	88	JMC 121K	14	JX 7046	91	KR 1728	52
HSC 173X	62	JMN 727	56	JX 9106	91	KRH 411P	88
HSD 76V	88	JN 5783	48	JXC 288	29	KRN 422	54
HSK 953	114	JNA 467	44	JXC 432	19	KRU 55F	76
HTB 656	44	JNB 416	47	JXN 370	91	KSK 270	56
HTF 586	44	JND 629	53	JY 124	108	KTA 986V	117
HTF 644B	54	JND 646	44	KAG 856	39	KTC 615	53
HTJ 521B	54	JND 728	65	KAH 407	36	KTD 768	53
HTT 487	83	JND 791	44	KAH 408	32	KTF 594	116
HUD 476S	52	JNK 681C	91	KAL 579	19	KTT 689	16

KTV 493	56	LMJ 653G	48	MLL 952	114	NKD 536	92
KTV 506	56	LN 4743	34	MLL 969	29	NKD 540	92
KUF 199F	103	LN 7270	93	MMN 302	92	NLE 534	29
KUS 607E	75	LNA 166G	99	MMW 354G	79	NLE 537	43
KVF 247V	21	LNN 89E	50	MN 2615	43	NLE 643	114
KVH 219	56	LOD 495	112	MNW 86	39	NLE 672	29
KVH 473E	39	LOG 301	16	MO 9324	14	NLE 939	106
KVO 429P	50	LOG 302	16	MOD 973	106	NLJ 268	75
KW 1961	32	LOU 48	72	MOD 978	75	NLJ 271	117
KW 2260	39	LOW 271	102	MOF 90	16	NLJ 272	75
KW 474	42	LPT 328	94	MOR 581	72	NLP 645	48
KW 7604	42	LRN 321J	96	MPK 693P	115	NMA 328D	65
KW xxx	56	LRN 60J	23	MPU 21	78	NMN 907	92
KWE 255	64	LRV 996	27	MRB 765	113	NMR 345	75
KWT 642D	39	LST 873	114	MRT 6P	36	NMY 634E	60
KXW 171	112	LSX 16P	62	MSD 407	54	NMY 646E	114
KXW 488	31	LTA 772	48	MSF 750P	62	NNB 125	46
KYE 905	115	LTA 813	107	MSU 252	87	NNB 547H	99
KYY 622	106	LTB 907	42	MTB 848	44	NNB 589H	99
KYY 628	114	LTC 774	44	MTC 540	96	NNC 854P	115
LA 9928	43	LTE 489P	54	MTE 639	59	NNC 855P	97
LAA 231	72	LTF 254	91	MTL 750	14	NNN 968	50
LAE 13	77	LTN 501	49	MTT 640	112	NNN 9P	115
LAK 309G	41	LTU 869	67	MUA 45P	41	NNU 123M	80
LAK 313G	41	LUC 210	29	MUA 865P	85	NNU 124M	80
LC 3701	43	LUO 47F	83	MUA 870P	41	NNU 234	75
LCD 52	32	LUO 595	108	MUN 742R	108	NNW 492	39
LDB 796	117	LUS 524E	60	MUR 217L	115	NOB 413M	107
LDJ 985	54	LVK 123	94	MXX 23	19	NOC 600R	107
LDN 96	54	LWB 383P	64	MXX 289	112	NOE 544R	21
LDP 945	109	LWB 388P	64	MXX 332	105	NOV 880G	107
LDS 201A	60	LWR 424	39	MXX 334	29	NPD 127L	105
LED 71P	54	LYF 377	114	MXX 364	43	NRG 154M	34
LEN 101	85	LYR 533	39	MXX 367	115	NRN 586	96
LF 9967	93	LYR 826	29	MXX 410	106	NSJ 502	60
LFM 302	116	LYR 910	29	MXX 430	106	NTF 466	53
LFM 717	116	LYR 915	105	MXX 434	105	NTT 661	83
LFM 724	116	LYR 969	112	MXX 489	105	NTT 679	83
LFM 734	117	MAF 544	108	MYA 590	29	NTW 942C	23
LFM 753	22	MAH 744	36	MZ 7396	67	NTY 416F	60
LFM 756	92	MAL 310	50	NAC 416F	52	NUB 609	39
LFR 529F	54	MCK 229J	85	NAE 3	79	NUB 93V	116
LFR 540G	91	MCN 30K	95	NAG 120G	60	NUD 105L	80
LFS 296F	103	MDG 227V	116	NAT 766A	64	NUW 567Y	43
LFS 480	59	MDJ 554E	54	NBB 628	32	NVK 341	94
LFW 326	42	MDJ 555E	54	NBN 436	75	NWU 265D	39
LG 2637	65	MDL 880R	37	NBU 494	46	NWW 89E	85
LHA 870F	18	MDT 222	56	NCK 338J	96	NXP 506	59
LHL 164F	85	MFN 898	31	NCS 16P	62	NXP 997	43
LHN 784	56	MFR 306P	97	NDB 356	117	NZE 598	67
LHN 860	74	MGB 286E	88	NDH 959	78	NZE 620	67
LHS 748V	88	MGE 183P	88	NDK 980	46	NZE 629	67
LHT 911	90	MHU 49	22	NDL 656R	62	O 9926	19
LHW 918	22	MHY 765	64	NDL 769G	74	OAS 287R	18
LIL 9929	62	MIL 7618	88	NDV 537G	83	OAX 9F	79
LJ 500	75	MJ 4549	72	NEA 101F	21	OBN 502R	101
LJ 9501	29	MJA 891G	46	NFM 67	22	OC 527	19
LJH 665	116	MJA 897G	46	NFS 176Y	62	OCK 985K	32
LJX 198	91	MJD 759	95	NG 1109	36	OD 5489	108
LJX 215	91	MKB 994	92	NHA 744	19	OD 5868	108
LLU 613	16	MLL 523	115	NHA 795	19	OD 7497	83
LLU 670	112	MLL 584	16	NHN 128	39	OD 7500	108
LLU 829	32	MLL 685	29	NHU 2	84	ODE 182	89
LLU 957	98	MLL 740	29	NJA 568W	101	ODL 400	37
LLU 987	98	MLL 817	106	NJO 703	51	ODV 404W	116
LMA 284	44	MLL 943	114	NJW 719E	21	OFC 205	51

Reg	No.	Reg	No.	Reg	No.	Reg	No.
OFC 393	51	PDU 125M	47	RFM 644	54	SPK 203M	29
OFC 902H	80	PFE 542V	42	RFU 689	79	SPT 65	94
OFM 957K	68	PFN 858	64	RHS 400W	62	SRB 424	47
OFN 721F	31	PFN 865	50	RKC 262	92	SRJ 328H	54
OFR 989M	18	PFR 346	54	RN 7588	96	SS 7486	58
OFS 777	59	PFR 554H	91	RN 7824	44	SS 7501	58
OFS 798	59	PGK 872	39	RN 8622	39	SSX 602V	62
OHK 432	42	PHA 370M	21	RNA 220J	99	STJ 847L	91
OJ 9347	16	PHN 699	94	RNA 236J	104	STO 523H	50
OJD 95R	115	PJX 232	39	ROD 765	91	SUK 3	19
OJO 727	80	PJX 35	85	RRN 405	90	SV 6107	96
OKW 515R	80	PJX 43	39	RRN 428	96	SVS 281	109
OLD 589	43	PND 460	46	RRS 46R	62	SVS 904	39
OLD 714	42	PNF 941J	99	RRU 901	75	SWS 671	59
OLJ 291	48	PNU 114K	80	RRU 903	16	SWS 715	59
OMS 244	87	POR 428	72	RRU 904	75	SXA 63K	60
ONE 744	54	POU 494	86	RTC 645L	54	SYG 561	39
ONF 865H	99	PRN 145	96	RTJ 422L	91	SYX 569F	103
ONO 59	42	PRN 79K	96	RU 2266	75	TBC 164	14
ONO 995	79	PRN 906	96	RU 8678	58	TBK 190K	27
OOX 816R	18	PRX 190B	103	RUF 186	82	TCD 374J	103
OP 237	16	PRX 200B	103	RUF 37R	103	TCD 376J	115
OPN 807	79	PRX 206B	103	RV 3411	27	TCD 383J	103
OPV 821	103	PSJ 480	54	RV 4649	27	TCD 490J	103
ORB 277	19	PSJ 825R	64	RV 6360	52	TCH 274L	21
ORC 545P	50	PTC 114C	46	RV 6368	27	TCK 465	96
ORJ 83W	46	PTD 640S	101	RWB 87	64	TCK 726	96
ORS 60R	62	PTE 944C	46	RWU 534R	89	TDH 912	22
ORU 230G	76	PTF 746L	97	SB 8155	16	TDH 914	56
ORV 989	27	PUF 165H	103	SBN 767	75	TDJ 612	54
OSJ 629R	62	PUM 149W	41	SCD 731N	103	TDK 322	64
OT 8283	72	PUO 331M	23	SCH 117X	50	TDK 686J	115
OT 8592	72	PV 817	35	SCH 237	22	TE 5110	66
OT 8898	72	PV 8270	36	SCS 333M	62	TE 5780	88
OTA 632G	21	PV 9371	36	SCS 335M	88	TE 7870	72
OTA 640G	107	PVH 931	78	SCS 366M	62	TE 8318	42
OTT 43	107	PW 8605	93	SDL 268	37	TET 135	64
OTT 55	48	PWL 413	51	SDX 57	23	TF 6860	39
OTV 137	56	PWL 999W	80	SFC 609	52	TF 818	42
OTV 161	50	Q507 OHR	22	SFC 610	52	TGM 214J	60
OU 1805	72	Q894 RCA	68	SFV 421	96	THL 261H	85
OU 9286	86	RAG 411	60	SG 2030	32	TIJ 687	116
OUM 727P	14	RAG 578	59	SGD 239	87	TJ 836	72
OV 4090	19	RAR 690J	104	SGD 241	87	TJO 56K	80
OV 4486	19	RB 4757	88	SGD 448	87	TMS 585H	60
OVL 473	105	RBC 345G	104	SGD 491	87	TNA 496	46
OWC 182D	79	RBW 87M	80	SGD 500	87	TNA 520	46
OWE 116	64	RC 2721	42	SGD 65	87	TNB 759K	99
OWE 271K	21	RC 4615	19	SGF 483L	79	TOB 986H	107
OWJ 353A	54	RC 8472	109	SHA 431	19	TOB 997H	107
OWJ 354A	54	RC 8575	56	SHA 645G	21	TPD 28S	115
OWS 620	59	RCH 518F	50	SHN 301	94	TPT 6R	115
OWT 776M	41	RCM 493	68	SJ 1340	58	TRJ 109	54
OWX 167	84	RCS 382	60	SKB 168	92	TRJ 112	46
OWY 750K	85	RCU 838S	95	SKB 224	92	TRN 481V	97
OZ 6686	67	RCV 283R	115	SKB 695G	92	TRN 731	39
PBC 734	47	RD 111	72	SLT 56	43	TRN 810V	97
PBN 668	54	RD 7127	78	SLT 57	43	TSK 763	113
PCG 888G	102	RDB 846	117	SLT 58	29	TTA 400H	102
PCG 889G	102	RDB 872	22	SMS 120P	62	TTD 386H	46
PCN 762	95	RDH 505	19	SND 460X	101	TTT 781	83
PCW 203J	95	RDS 597W	88	SO 3740	58	TUO 217J	106
PDH 808	19	REN 116	46	SOA 674S	105	TUO 482	105
PDJ 269L	54	RFE 416	42	SOE 913H	107	TUO 497	79
PDL 515	37	RFM 408	79	SOU 456	72	TUO 74J	83
PDL 519	37	RFM 641	68	SOU 465	72	TUP 329R	95

TUP 859	94	VD 3433	58	WDA 986T	107	XON 41J	18
TV 9333	56	VDL 264K	37	WDF 569	21	XRU 277K	76
TWH 807K	75	VDV 752	117	WDK 562T	116	XSL 228A	114
TWH 809K	75	VDV 753	117	WDS 115V	88	XSL 945A	59
TWL 928	52	VDV 760	64	WEX 685M	85	XSN 25A	60
TWS 910T	23	VDV 798	83	WFM 801K	41	XTA 839	83
TWT 123	85	VDV 817	108	WFN 513	31	XTF 98D	54
TWW 766F	41	VER 262L	52	WG 2373	113	XTP 287L	27
TWY 8	84	VF 2788	35	WG 3260	58	XU 7498	93
TXJ 507K	46	VF 8157	35	WG 8107	58	XUF 141	103
TY 9608	84	VFS 542V	62	WG 8790	58	XUO 721	83
TYD 122G	115	VFU 864J	60	WG 9180	64	XVU 341M	99
TYD 888	59	VG 5541	107	WH 1553	42	XVU 352M	46
UCS 659	60	VH 2088	88	WHL 970	85	XVU 363M	99
UCX 275	60	VH 6188	75	WHN 411G	95	XWX 795	56
UDT 455F	57	VH 6217	75	WKG 287	117	XX 9591	29
UF 1517	14	VJO 201X	80	WLT 371	114	YBD 201	113
UF 6473	14	VK 5401	49	WLT 506	16	YDB 453L	99
UF 6805	14	VKB 711	92	WLT 529	109	YDK 590	46
UF 7428	14	VKB 841	92	WLT 759	88	YDL 135T	37
UFC 430K	52	VKB 900	92	WLT 900	112	YFM 283L	79
UFF 178	59	VL 1263	42	WLT 991	54	YFR 351	90
UFJ 292	94	VLT 140	48	WNG 864H	21	YG 7831	93
UFJ 296	83	VLT 163	114	WNL 259A	95	YHT 958	22
UFM 52F	68	VLT 216	114	WRA 12	64	YHY 80	77
UFM 53F	79	VLT 235	114	WRH 294J	114	YLG 717F	41
UFX 718	50	VLW 444G	105	WRJ 179	103	YLJ 147	75
UGB 193W	88	VM 4439	44	WRU 702B	117	YLJ 286	32
UGB 196W	88	VMJ 967S	115	WT 7101	39	YNX 478	52
UHA 255	19	VML 5G	88	WT 7108	49	YOX 130K	26
UHA 956H	21	VMP 10G	60	WT 9156	88	YOX 133K	107
UHA 969H	18	VMP 8G	60	WTE 155D	60	YPL 105T	116
UHA 981H	21	VNB 101L	46	WTS 266T	62	YPL 78T	116
UHY 359	22	VNB 177L	99	WTS 270T	88	YPL 92T	116
UHY 362	107	VNB 203L	99	WTS 429A	103	YPT 796	95
UI 8511	67	VO 6806	48	WV 1209	35	YR 3844	43
UK 9978	22	VO 8846	50	WW 4688	78	YRC 194	50
UKA 562H	92	VOD 107S	83	WWH 43L	99	YRT 898H	32
UKE 830X	52	VOD 550K	83	WWJ 754M	57	YSG 101	60
ULS 640X	88	VPH 53S	116	WWY 115G	104	YSL 334	113
ULS 716X	62	VPT 598R	95	WZJ 724	67	YTE 826	32
ULS 717X	62	VR 5742	44	XAK 355L	41	YWB 494M	52
UMA 370	46	VRC 612Y	50	XBU 1S	101	YWL 134K	80
UMP 227	29	VRD 193	57	XC 8059	43	YYB 239H	104
UMP 903M	115	VRU 124J	76	XCW 955R	97	YYJ 914	60
UO 2331	108	VSC 86	59	XDH 516G	21	ZC 714	66
UOU 417H	86	VTU 76	39	XDH 519G	22	ZD 7163	67
UOU 419H	86	VUD 30X	80	XDH 56G	21	ZH 3926	67
UP 551	49	VUD 348H	80	XDH 72	78	ZH 3937	67
USV 324	103	VUP 328	95	XEM 898W	68	ZH 4538	67
UTC 672	46	VV 5696	78	XFM 42G	60	ZI 9708	66
UTF 732M	97	VVF 543	79	XG 9304	58	ZJ 5904	26
UTN 501Y	95	VVP 911	21	XGA 8J	88	ZJ 5933	67
UTU 596J	19	VW 203	108	XHA 482	19	ZL 2718	67
UU 6646	29	VY 957	44	XHA 496	19	ZL 6816	67
UUA 214	39	VZI 44	67	XHO 370	72	ZO 6819	67
UUF 110J	82	VZL 179	67	XJA 534L	99	ZO 6857	67
UUF 116J	103	W 963	50	XKC 862K	92	ZO 6881	67
UVL 873M	42	WAJ 112	59	XLG 477	39	ZO 6949	67
UWX 981F	104	WBR 246	39	XLV 140W	55	ZO 6960	26
UXD 129G	105	WBR 248	95	XM 7399	43	ZU 9241	67
UZG 100	67	WCG 104	86	XMS 252R	62	ZV 1461	103
UZH 258	26	WDA 700T	18	XMS 422Y	88	ZY 1715	26
VBA 151S	54	WDA 835T	107	XNG 770S	36	ZY 79	67
VBD 310H	104	WDA 956T	107	XNX 136H	18		

Index of Museums, Collections and Heritage Bus Services

Rexquote Heritage fleet is varied, and contains many unique survivors like this ex-Maidstone & District Weymann-bodied AEC Reliance converted to open-top in 1974. *John C. Walker*

* Operators of Heritage Bus Services

Well-known for its many appearances in the TV series 'Heartbeat' is ex-United BG413, an ECW-bodied Bristol L5G saloon. *Aycliffe & District Bus Preservation Society*